Property of
Raymond C. Vasko

Principles of

Scientific and Technical Writing

Principles
of
SCIENTIFIC
and
TECHNICAL
WRITING

JACKSON E. MORRIS

University of California, Los Angeles
North American Aviation, Inc.

New York   San Francisco   St. Louis
Toronto   Sydney   London

McGRAW-HILL BOOK COMPANY

Principles of

A
SCIENTIFIC AND TECHNICAL WRITING

Printed in the United States of America

Library of Congress catalog card number: 65-28824

1234567890 PN 721069876

43145

Preface

THIS TEXTBOOK was written for use in a course in scientific and technical writing which the author gave for several years at the University of California, Los Angeles, in the Engineering Extension Program. The students who attended the lectures were drawn from varied backgrounds. Perhaps 50 percent of them were scientists and engineers who wanted to improve their writing as a basis for job advancement. Perhaps 25 percent were practicing technical writers and editors, drawn from the aerospace, petroleum, and electronics industries of southern California. Perhaps 15 percent were secretaries, journalists, and advertising writers who wished to become technical writers, and 10 percent were foreign-born engineers who wished to improve their knowledge of the English language.

These students could best be served, it seemed, by a series of lectures and exercises which emphasized the cultivation of a simple, correct, and vigorous scientific and technical writing style. This was the "writing" aspect of the course. The "scientific and technical" aspect of the course was embodied in lectures on such topics as technical reports, scientific papers, duplicating and printing processes, library research, and the use of tables and illustrations.

To serve this second end, various industry and institutional style

v

guides were presented and studied. Unfortunately, these were found to differ in many respects, such as compounding, capitalization, abbreviation, and report format. Since most of the students worked for one industry or another, they were advised to follow the company style at work.

The wide variation in recommended forms and usage is one of the problems of scientific and technical writing, and, until more agreement can be achieved, the author feels that students can spend their classroom time most profitably in the cultivation of a skilled writing style. If an authoritative style guide is required, the inexpensive *Style Manual* of the American Institute of Physics can be obtained. Many recommendations of this manual are presented in the text.

Another problem found in technical writing, particularly in the aerospace industry, results from the fact that the finished page usually is the work not of one skilled writer but of several semi-skilled writers. The practice is to edit material not once, but several times for several purposes, such as for style, for company policy, and for technical accuracy. This occurs because of the very large volume of reports published and because of the attempt, laudable or not, to mechanize the editorial process. Report writing is regarded by many engineering managers as a production process, like assembling a car. The outcome tends to be acre-like pages of the flat, stale prose of officialdom. This prose is regarded as safe because it is dressed in the protective colors of such empty, fashionable phrases as are current in engineering jargon. Its lack of natural vigor or trenchancy only wearies the working engineer who, finally, must read and make sense of it.

This textbook, then, emphasizes vigorous, clear style in the first place and technical procedures in the second place. Two other aspects of its planning are worth mentioning. It (1) draws on the voluminous publishing experience of various aerospace companies and (2) reports some of the remarkable results which have been obtained lately in computer analysis and processing of language. The scientific and engineering writer is now discovering that he must, willy-nilly, use these data processing techniques in advanced, large-scale programs.

An attempt has been made in this textbook to adapt formal English rules of syntax to suit the analytical bent of the engineer.

This can be done with particular felicity in the examination of word classes and sentence structure. Classification trees are presented (in an appendix) which array these bewildering elements geometrically. The engineer, typically, has a spatially oriented mind. He tends to visualize his thoughts. Geometrical shapes organize and move in his brain in a quick parade as he thinks. When such frowzy creatures of the cave as words can be lured into the light of geometry and made to show their capabilities, then the engineer is well served.

The contributions of J. A. Luttrell, Jr., and Nat Miller to many of the ideas discussed in this book are gratefully acknowledged.

JACKSON E. MORRIS

This book is dedicated to my father,

OLIVER S. MORRIS

Contents

1 Historical Perspective, 1

1.1   *Ancient Sources, 2*
1.1.1   *Egyptian Medicine, 2*
1.1.2   *Greek Poetry, 3*
1.1.3   *Greek History, 4*
1.1.4   *Greek Philosophy, 6*
1.1.5   *Roman Engineering, 6*
1.2   *English Sources, 8*
1.2.1   *Medieval Science, 8*
1.2.2   *Renaissance Science, 9*
1.2.3   *Modern Prose Sources, 10*
1.2.4   *Popular Science Tradition, 11*
1.3   *American Sources, 12*
1.3.1   *Early American Science, 12*
1.3.2   *Nineteenth Century Science, 14*
1.3.3   *Aerodynamics, Missiles, and Space Flight, 16*

2 Qualitative Aspects, 20

2.1   *Knowledge of Subject, 22*
2.2   *Knowledge of Audience, 24*

2.3   *Organization of Material,* 26

2.4   *Effective Writing Style,* 28

2.5   *Motivation in Writing,* 31

Characteristics of Language, 33

3.1   *Language and Communication,* 34

3.1.1   *Language and Mathematics,* 34

3.1.2   *Language and Memory,* 35

3.1.3   *Language and Information Theory,* 36

3.1.4   *Language and Symbolic Logic,* 36

3.1.5   *Language and Computers,* 37

3.1.5.1   *Translation,* 37

3.1.5.2   *Language and Electronic Data Processing,* 39

3.1.5.3   *Library Indexing and Coding,* 39

3.2   *Development of Language,* 40

3.2.1   *Language Sources,* 40

3.2.2   *Contributions of Linguistics,* 42

3.2.3   *Symbolic Writing,* 43

3.2.4   *Phonetic Writing,* 43

3.3   *Language Structural Elements,* 45

3.3.1   *Words and Definition,* 45

3.3.2   *Extended Definition,* 46

3.3.3   *Modern Definition,* 47

3.3.4   *Word Classes,* 49

3.3.5   *Word Group Classes,* 49

Choice of Person and Tense, 51

4.1   *Choice of Person,* 51

4.1.1   *Use of* It, 52

4.1.2   *Use of* You, 55

4.1.3   *Use of* We *and* I, 56

4.1.4   *Impersonal Usage and Passive Voice,* 58

4.1.5   *Examples of Passive Construction,* 58

4.1.6   *Recommended Usage,* 60

4.2   *Choice of Tense,* 62

4.2.1   *Rules for Choice,* 62

4.2.2   *Comments on Tense,* 63

4.2.3   *Use of Conditional Statements,* 64

 Effective Sentences, 66

5.1   *Sentence Variety,* 66

5.2   *Sentence Complexity,* 67

5.2.1   *Measures of Complexity,* 67

5.2.1.1 *Sentence Length,* 67

5.2.1.2 *Sentence Indexes,* 67

5.2.2   *Sentence Symmetry,* 68

5.2.3   *Sentence Memory Level,* 69

5.2.4   *Sentence Order and Clarity,* 70

5.2.5   *Logical Signposts,* 72

5.2.6   *Recommendations for Clarity,* 73

5.3   *Parallel Structure,* 74

5.3.1   *Coordinate Constructions,* 74

5.3.2   *Lists and Enumerations,* 75

5.3.3   *Series Construction,* 75

5.4   *Subordinate Structure,* 77

5.4.1   *Lack of Subordination,* 77

5.4.2   *Faulty Subordination,* 77

5.4.3   *Subordination of Details,* 78

5.5   *Emphasis,* 78

5.5.1   *Emphasis by Statement,* 78

5.5.2   *Emphasis by Position,* 79

5.5.3   *Emphasis by Proportion,* 79

5.5.4   *Emphasis by Style,* 80

5.5.5   *Emphasis by Repetition; Paragraph Unity,* 80

Sentence Criticism, 83

6.1   *Wordy Sentences,* 83

6.1.1   *Writing with Phrases,* 83

6.1.2   *Redundancy,* 84

6.1.3   *Weak Word Choice,* 85

6.1.4   *Use of Cult Words,* 86

6.1.5   *Trivial Statements,* 87

  6.2   *Confusing Sentences,* 88

6.2.1   *Incomplete Sentences (Ellipsis),* 89

6.2.2   *Faulty Word Choice,* 90

6.2.3   *Faulty Classification,* 91

6.2.4   *Modification and Sentence Order,* 92

6.2.4.1   *Dangling Modifiers,* 92

6.2.4.2   *Misplaced Modifiers,* 93

6.2.4.3   *Split Constructions,* 95

6.2.5   *Faulty Comparison,* 96

  6.3   *Errors of Inflection and Reference,* 97

6.3.1   *Classification of Errors,* 97

6.3.2   *Errors of Number (Singular and Plural),* 98

6.3.3   *Errors of Ambiguous Reference,* 100

7 *Logic in Writing,* 102

  7.1   *Types of Nonfictional Writing,* 102

  7.2   *Expository Writing,* 103

7.2.1   *Analysis and Synthesis,* 103

7.2.2   *Example of Analytic Explanation,* 104

7.2.3   *Example of Synthetic Explanation,* 105

  7.3   *Argumentative Writing,* 107

7.3.1   *Deductive Reasoning,* 108

7.3.2   *Errors in Deductive Reasoning,* 109

7.3.3   *Common Verbal Fallacies,* 110

7.3.4   *Inductive Reasoning,* 111

7.3.5   *Errors in Inductive Reasoning,* 113

7.3.6   *Statistical Induction Processes,* 114

  7.4   *Descriptive and Narrative Writing,* 114

8 *Organization of Written Material,* 117

8.1 *Introduction to Problem,* 117
8.2 *Statement of Scope,* 118
8.3 *Nature of Outlining,* 119
8.3.1 *General Outlining Sequences,* 119
8.3.2 *Example of Typical Sequence,* 120
8.4 *Discussion of Outline Sequences,* 121
8.4.1 *Order of Relative Magnitude, Importance, or Priority,* 121
8.4.2 *Order of Formal Logic,* 123
8.4.2.1 *Order of Deduction,* 123
8.4.2.2 *Order of Induction,* 124
8.4.3 *Order of Time Sequence,* 125
8.4.4 *Order of Motion or Flow,* 126
8.4.5 *Order of Operational Steps,* 131
8.4.6 *Order of Definition,* 133
8.4.7 *Random and Artificial Order,* 134
8.5 *Framework Sections of Report,* 135
8.5.1 *Preliminary Sections,* 136
8.5.2 *Concluding Sections,* 138
8.6 *Outline Headings,* 139
8.6.1 *Decimal Headings,* 139
8.6.2 *Numeral-Letter Headings,* 140
8.7 *Summary and Remarks,* 141

9 *Criticism of Short Reports,* 142

9.1 *Rules for Criticism,* 142
9.1.1 *Style and Grammar,* 143
9.1.2 *Writing and Editing,* 144
9.2 *Criticism of Expository Report,* 144
9.2.1 *Specimen Expository Report,* 144
9.2.2 *General Criticism of Specimen Report,* 145
9.2.3 *Detailed Criticism of Specimen Report,* 147
9.2.4 *Specimen Report Rewritten,* 148

9.3   *Criticism of Proposal,* 149

9.3.1 *Specimen Proposal,* 149

9.3.2 *General Criticism of Specimen Proposal,* 151

9.3.3 *Detailed Criticism of Specimen Proposal,* 152

9.3.4 *Specimen Proposal Rewritten,* 153

9.3.5 *Comments on Terminology,* 154

9.4   *Criticism of Narrative Report,* 155

9.4.1 *Specimen Trip Report,* 155

9.4.2 *Criticism of Specimen Trip Report,* 156

9.4.3 *Specimen Trip Report Rewritten,* 157

9.5   *Criticism of Analytical Report,* 158

9.5.1 *Specimen Analytical Report,* 158

9.5.2 *Criticism of Specimen Report,* 159

9.5.3 *Analytical Report Rewritten,* 160

 Program Documentation Requirements, 162

10.1   *Documentation Survey,* 162

10.2   *Proposals,* 163

10.2.1 *Study Proposals,* 163

10.2.2 *Development Proposals,* 164

10.2.3 *Management Proposals,* 165

10.3   *Program Planning Documents,* 166

10.3.1 *Program Summary Plan,* 167

10.3.2 *Facilities Plan; Manufacturing Plan,* 168

10.3.3 *Test Plan,* 168

10.3.4 *Other Program Plans,* 169

10.4   *Specifications,* 171

10 5   *Investigation Reports,* 172

10.5.1 *Test Reports,* 172

10.5.2 *Experimental Investigation Reports,* 172

10.5.3 *Data Reports,* 173

10.5.4 *Study Reports,* 174

10.6   *Quality Control and Reliability Reports,* 175

10.6.1 *Quality Control Reports,* 175

10.6.2 *Reliability Reports,* 176

10.7 *Progress Reports,* 176
10.8 *Procedures,* 177
10.9 *Handbooks and Manuals,* 178

 Technical Publications Organization, 181

11.1 *Publications Department,* 181
11.1.1 *Survey of Technical Report Functions,* 181
11.1.2 *Other Publications Functions,* 183
11.1.3 *Technical Reports Group,* 183
11.1.4 *Use of Style Guides,* 185
11.1.5 *Typing and Illustrations Groups,* 187
11.1.5.1 *Typing Group,* 187
11.1.5.2 *Illustrations Group,* 188
11.1.6 *Reproduction and Printing Services,* 189
11.1.6.1 *Electrostatic Reproduction Processes,* 189
11.1.6.2 *Ammonia Vapor Reproduction Processes,* 190
11.1.6.3 *Spirit Reproduction Processes,* 191
11.1.6.4 *Printing Processes,* 191
11.2 *Report Editing,* 192
11.2.1 *Analyzing the Rough Draft,* 192
11.2.2 *Obtaining Report Reviews,* 193
11.2.3 *Problems of Style,* 194
11.3 *Report Processing,* 195
11.3.1 *Processing Survey,* 195
11.3.2 *Report Distribution List,* 196
11.3.3 *Review and Approval Signatures,* 197
11.3.4 *Report Legal Review,* 197
11.3.5 *Arranging for Printing,* 198
11.3.6 *Mailing the Report,* 199

Scientific Papers and Theses, 200

12.1 *Problems of Scientific Writing,* 200
12.1.1 *Verbal and Numerical Analysis,* 201
12.1.2 *Problems of Compression,* 202

12.1.3 *Caution in Writing,* 203

12.1.4 *Loss of Grammatical Coupling,* 203

12.2 *Methods of Organization,* 204

12.2.1 *Survey of Scientific Papers,* 204

12.2.2 *Experimental Papers,* 205

12.2.3 *Theoretical Papers,* 205

12.2.4 *Additional Information on Organization,* 206

12.3 *The Thesis,* 207

12.3.1 *Selecting Thesis Topic,* 207

12.3.2 *Thesis Research,* 208

12.3.3 *Organization of Thesis Material,* 208

12.3.4 *Rewriting Thesis as Scientific Paper,* 209

12.4 *Manuscript Presentation and Proof,* 210

12.4.1 *Work Sheet for Contributors to Journals,* 210

12.4.2 *Concluding Remarks,* 213

13 *Library Research and Reference,* 214

13.1 *Research and Reference Functions,* 214

13.1.1 *Nature of Research Problems,* 215

13.1.2 *Nature of Documentation,* 215

13.1.3 *Traditional Card Catalogs,* 216

13.1.4 *Traditional Subject Classification,* 217

13.1.4.1 *Dewey Decimal Classification,* 217

13.1.4.2 *Library of Congress Classification,* 218

13.1.5 *Reference Books,* 219

13.1.6 *Abstract Services,* 220

13.1.7 *Technical Library Problems,* 220

13.2 *Information Retrieval Theory and Application,* 221

13.2.1 *Information Retrieval Functions,* 221

13.2.1.1 *Introduction,* 221

13.2.1.2 *Document Selecting and Abstracting,* 222

13.2.1.3 *Indexing and Cataloging,* 223

13.2.1.4 *Searching and Coding,* 224

13.2.1.5 *Storing Documents,* 224

13.2.1.6 *Presentation and Dissemination,* 225

13.3 *Special Report Catalogs,* 226

13.3.1 *DDC Technical Abstract Bulletin,* 226

13.3.2 *NASA Scientific and Technical Aerospace Reports,* 227

 Grammatical Terminology, 231

 Structure of Word Groups, 245

Index, 251

Principles of

Scientific and Technical Writing

Historical Perspective

The modern student of scientific and technical writing is fortunate to inherit a tradition of excellence which was established in this country by a few brilliant and lonely men. The pioneer names that come to mind include such isolated workers as Benjamin Franklin, Joseph Henry, Willard Gibbs, Samuel Langley, and Robert Goddard. In this chapter it will be shown that, in early Greece and in England, a continuing scientific tradition was established in which the great minds of the age participated naturally, supported by public interest and by royal patronage.

In the United States, on the other hand, the scientist and engineer tended at first to work alone, with little public notice. Only in the period which began with World War II did scientific and technical writing receive public or governmental acclaim and support. The modern writer in this field thus inherits a tradition of excellence won painfully by the labors of a few brilliant men.

The review of writing tradition which follows names only a few of those worthy of mention. It is intended principally to show the scientific and technical writer the continuing dignity and purpose of his profession.

1.1   ANCIENT SOURCES

1.1.1   Egyptian Medicine

The urge to express himself led primitive man first to develop speech and then to invent writing. Language at first was probably directed toward the satisfaction of immediate needs and drives, such as love, fear, and hunger. Gradually, however, writers learned to shape verbal models of the universe of our common experience, and today, as used in scientific and technical writing, language serves this need entirely. According to the noted linguist Joshua Whatmough, "Language is the means by which man symbolizes and orders his concepts of the universe."* The ability of language to express facts and scientific truths, quite apart from immediate needs, arose very slowly. The first known writings of this nature dealt with study of the human body by Egyptian physicians of the Pyramid Age (3000–2500 B.C.). As you read the following translation of one document, note the sturdy, workmanlike quality of the prose, well adequate for its purpose, and the effectively repeated sentence forms.

> If thou examinest a man having a break in the column of his nose, his nose being disfigured, and a depression being in it, while the swelling that is on it protrudes, and he had discharged blood from both his nostrils, thou shouldst say concerning him: "One having a break in the column of his nose. An ailment which I will treat."
> Thou shouldst cleanse it for him with two plugs of linen. Thou shouldst place two other plugs of linen saturated with grease in the inside of his two nostrils. Thou shouldst put him at his mooring stakes until the swelling is drawn out. Thou shouldst apply for him stiff rolls of linen by which his nose is held fast. Thou shouldst treat him afterward with lint, every day until he recovers.†

*Joshua Whatmough, *Language: A Modern Synthesis*, Secker and Warburg, Ltd., London, 1956, p. 83.

†F. R. Moulton and J. J. Schifferes, *The Autobiography of Science*, Doubleday & Company, Inc., Garden City, New York, 1960, p. 4.

2

The earliest extensive examples of recorded language come to us from the Greeks, and it is these writings, primarily historical, which are most influential in shaping our own ideas about language.   Homer's *Iliad* and *Odyssey* (composed about 800 B.C.) are epic poems dealing with the last year of the Trojan War and the wanderings of Odysseus after the Trojan War.   The style is emotional, which suggests the author is more interested in making us participate in the characters' experiences than in recording facts. This emotional participation of the reader or author (Homer recited his works and they were recorded later) is still the aim of poetry, novels, stories, and plays—in fact, of all fictional works. The teaching of history and morals may, of course, be implicit in such works, but this teaching is not the primary aim.

An examination of "technical writing" passages from the *Iliad* shows that, even in discussing the making of a shield, Homer sought not to instruct his audience but to astonish or overawe them with the shield's strength and magnificence.   The following passage, from Pope's translation, depicts the blacksmith of the gods, Vulcan, at work:

> Thus having said, the father of the fires
> To the black labors of his forge retires.
> Soon as he bade them blow, the bellows turned
> Their iron mouths; and where the furnace burn'd . . .
> They raise a tempest, or they gently blow;
> In hissing flames huge silver bars are rolled,
> And stubborn brass, and tin, and solid gold;
> Before, deep-fix'd, the eternal anvils stand;
> The ponderous hammer loads his better hand,
> His left with tongs turns the vex'd metal round,
> And thick, strong strokes, the doubling vaults rebound.
> Then first he form'd the immense and solid shield;
> Rich various artifice emblazed the field . . .

This passage is difficult reading and, of course, is related to technical writing in little more than subject.   Vulcan is shown to hold the tongs in his left hand and the hammer in his right, but the rest of the information is of doubtful value to anyone who wants to construct a stout shield.   True technical writing in primitive communities was probably confined to inscriptions on monuments, to medical directions, to instructions associated with maps and deeds, and to warehouse tallies. Greek warehouse lists itemizing such trade commodities as wine, olive oil, and clay vessels have, in fact, come to us from excavations at the site of the palace of a primitive king, thought to be Nestor, whom Homer portrays. These rough, honest trade lists do more to indicate to modern scholars the sources of Greek wealth and, to some extent, of Greek culture than even Homer does.

1.1.3   Greek History

The first steps in divorcing facts from opinion and emotion in Greek formal writing were probably taken by Greek historians, most notably by Herodotus (485–425 B.C.). Herodotus, called the father of history, wrote the first extensive body of Greek prose, setting forth the chronicles, legends, and topography of the known world. His purpose, as he states, was "to prevent the great and wonderful actions of the Greeks and the Barbarians from losing their due meed of glory; and withal to put on record what were their grounds for feud."

A significant difference in views is presented in this statement. The first part, dealing with "great and wonderful actions," represents the primitive, emotional view of history and science. The second part, an afterthought following a dry "withal," offhandedly gives the modern point of view: "put on record their grounds for feud." Why must anything be put on record? Only for later critical study, it would seem. It is the birth of this critical spirit for which the early Greeks are justly praised.

The historian who followed, Thucydides (471–400 B.C.), has been called the first modern thinker. Inspired directly by Herodotus, Thucydides made his purpose the refinement of putting things on record, historically. His *The Peloponnesian War* (Crawley translation) is an admirable study of man's actions during war and siege. Because he assiduously traced down facts, because he shrewdly confined all judgment to the facts, and because he wrote and rewrote, constantly narrowing and sharpening his narrative, Thucydides' history is unsurpassed for penetration and veracity even today.

4

In the following quotation from Thucydides, which describes a siege conducted by the Lacedaemonians (Peloponnesians), under King Archidamus, against the resourceful Plataeans, there is some confusion about the reference word *they*, but the reader should have little difficulty in sorting the references out. The topic is a fairly complex one dealing with two armies which are building different structures against the city wall of Plataea, but for opposite reasons.

After this appeal to the gods Archidamus put his army in motion. First he enclosed the town with a palisade formed of the fruit-trees which they cut down, to prevent further egress from Plataea; next day they threw up a mound against the city, hoping that the largeness of the force employed would insure the speedy reduction of the place. They accordingly cut down timber from Cithaeron, and built it up on either side, laying it like lattice-work to serve as a wall to keep the mound from spreading abroad, and carried to it wood and stones and earth and whatever other material might help to complete it. They continued to work at the mound for seventy days and nights without intermission, being divided into relief parties to allow some being employed in carrying while others took sleep and refreshment; the Lacedaemonian officer attached to each contingent keeping the men to the work. But the Plataeans observing the progress of the mound, constructed a wall of wood and fixed it upon that part of the city wall against which the mound was being erected, and built up bricks inside it which they took from the neighboring houses. The timbers served to bind the building together, and to prevent its becoming weak as it advanced in height; it had also a covering of skins and hides, which protected the wood-work against the attacks of burning missiles and allowed the men to work in safety. Thus the wall was raised to a great height, and the mound opposite made no less rapid progress. The Plataeans also thought of another expedient; they pulled out part of the wall upon which the mound abutted, and carried the earth into the city.

Discovering this the Peloponnesians twisted up clay in wattles of reed and threw it into the breach formed in the mound, in order to give it consistency and prevent its being carried away like the soil. Stopped in this way the Plataeans changed their mode of operation, and digging a mine from the town calculated their way under the mound, and began to carry off its material as before. This went on for a long while without the enemy outside finding it out, so that for all they threw on the top their mound made no progress in proportion, being carried away from beneath and constantly settling down in the vacuum.

1.1.4   Greek Philosophy

Thucydides' great work undoubtedly influenced other Greek thinkers. Of all the scholars who followed, including Plato (philosopher and master of prose style), Euclid (great geometer), and Hippocrates (physician and medical writer), only Aristotle (384–322 B.C.) will be quoted, for Aristotle added a new dimension to scientific writing. He is the first Greek to move man from the center of the stage to the wings; that is, to attempt to describe and analyze all the objects of nature without regard for human advantage or feeling. True scientific writing (writing by scientists for scientists) thus probably appeared first with Aristotle. Such writing represents a revolution in man's viewpoint.

The passage from Aristotle which follows must have shocked conservative Greeks, because it discusses insects as formally and seriously as religion or history might be discussed. The passage, from *Parts of Animals*, appears to contain some early observations on flight dynamics. The prose is flexible and clear.

> As for a tail sting, nature has given it to insects that are of a fierce disposition and to no others. Sometimes this instrument is lodged inside the body, as in bees and wasps. This position is a necessary consequence of those insects being made for flight. For, were their piercer or sting external and of a delicate make, it would very easily get hurt. If, on the other hand, it were of a stouter build, as in scorpions, its weight would interfere with flight.

After Aristotle, one final step in creating the modern scientific method of research remained to be taken: the direct comparison of theory with planned experiment. This step was reserved for the renaissance in learning (about 1300–1500). During this period Galileo demonstrated, by dropping stones from the Leaning Tower, that Aristotle's law of falling bodies (heavier bodies fall faster) was incorrect. One brilliant Sicilian, Archimedes (287–212 B.C.), had understood the requirements of experiment, but unfortunately his thinking was so far ahead of his time that he did not have wide influence.

1.1.5   Roman Engineering

The Romans, who succeeded the Greeks, contributed more to engineering than to science, and so developed the first technical

6

writers. (Here, technical writing can be defined as writing by engineers for engineers.) Roman aqueducts, tunnels, bridges, and public buildings remain today as impressive monuments. Roman prose works on the practical arts also remain; for instance, books on agriculture, jurisprudence, medicine, natural science, and architecture. Many eminent Romans were practical writers. Julius Caesar (100–44 B.C.), for instance, in his *Commentaries on the Gallic War*, produced a notable description of the building in ten days of a floating military bridge over the Rhine River.

Another noted Roman engineer was Vitruvius, who wrote in the first century B.C. Vitruvius dominated one aspect of engineering—architecture—more than one man has ever done. For sixteen centuries the ten volumes which he wrote on this topic were the bibles of the builder. Vitruvius can be considered a true technical writer since his extensive works included compilations of other known sources. He wrote on all aspects of building: materials, design, structure, analysis, aesthetics, and even on acoustics. A passage from his *De Architectura* is quoted, dealing with the use of logs in building and showing his wide range of interest.

Among the Colchians in Pontus, where there are forests in plenty, they lay down entire trees flat on the ground to the right and the left, leaving between them a space to suit the length of the trees, and then place above these another pair of trees, resting on the ends of the former and at right angles with them. These four trees enclose the space for the dwelling. Then upon these they place sticks of timber one after the other on the four sides, crossing each other at the angles, and so, proceeding with their walls of trees laid perpendicularly above the lowest, they build up high towers. The interstices which are left on account of the thickness of the building material are stopped up with chips and mud. As for the roofs, by cutting away the ends of the crossbeams and making them converge gradually as they lay them across, they bring them up to the top from the four sides in the shape of a pyramid. They cover it with leaves and mud, and thus construct the roofs of their towers in a rude form of the "tortoise" style.

On the other hand, the Phrygians, who live in an open country, have no forests and consequently lack timber. They therefore select a natural hillock, run a trench through the middle of it, dig passages, and extend the interior space as widely as the site admits. Over it they build a pyramidal roof of logs fastened together, and this they cover with reeds and brushwood, heaping up very high mounds of earth above their dwellings. Thus their fashion in houses makes their winters very warm and their summers very cool.*

Other Roman scientific and technical writers worthy of mention are Lucretius (98–55 B.C.), who wrote poetry about atomic theory; Pliny the Elder (A.D. 23–79), who wrote exhaustively on natural history, military tactics, and history; and Galen (A.D. 130–201), who was the greatest medical authority of the age.

1.2   ENGLISH SOURCES

1.2.1   Medieval Science

The English have been praised as scientists for developing the experimental aspect of research, as well as the theoretical. Most ancient people tended to regard the physical labor connected with experiments as plebeian, or undignified, and so remained armchair scientists. This defect led their science astray, and it remained for such great men as Copernicus, Galileo, and certain English scientists to show that theory and experiment must go hand in hand.

The emphasis on experiment appeared with the first significant English writer on science, the friar Roger Bacon (1214–1294). Bacon (who wrote in Latin) can be translated as follows:

> There are two methods by which we acquire knowledge — argument and experiment. Argument allows us to draw conclusions, and may cause us to admit the conclusion; but it gives us no proof, nor does it remove doubt, and cause the mind to rest in conscious possession of truth, unless the truth is discovered by way of experience, e.g., if any man who had never seen fire were to prove by satisfactory argument that fire burns and destroys things, the hearer's mind would not rest satisfied, nor would he avoid fire; until by putting his hand or some combustible thing into it, he proved by actual experiment what the argument laid down.

The first great writer of prose in the English language was the poet and storyteller Geoffrey Chaucer (author of *The Canterbury Tales*). Chaucer, oddly enough, wrote a treatise in 1391 on the use of the astrolabe, an ancient type of sextant, solely for the edification of his small son, Louis. This treatise, though unfinished, gives such clear, accurate, and thorough instructions that Chaucer

*By permission from Morris Hicky Morgan, *Vitruvius: The Ten Books on Architecture*, Harvard University Press, Cambridge, Mass., © 1914.

may well be called an equipment-handbook writer. The treatise is divided into five parts. The first part introduces the instrument and its chief components. The second part explains the operations of certain components. The third part instructs Louis in the use of stellar tables of position; that is, in latitude, longitude, and time. The fourth part presents certain theories regarding the motion of heavenly bodies, and the fifth part is an introduction to astrology and navigation.

Chaucer was a witty writer and his statement of purpose shows this talent. The following passage is rewritten from his fourteenth-century prose:

> Now I pray that every person who reads or hears this treatise will excuse my simple writing and my repetition for two reasons. The first reason is that I must write in a simple manner to explain difficult ideas to such a small boy. The second reason is that it seems better to write a good idea down twice in case he forgets it once.

Another Englishman named Bacon, the eminent Francis Bacon (1561–1626), is credited to a large degree with the discovery of the inductive method in science; that is, with the use of controlled experiments to detect and prove general laws of nature. The Aristotelian deductive method, which he challenged, was to discover the laws of nature by simple deduction from general philosophical principles determined by instinct. The two logical processes, induction and deduction, therefore became firmly established early in English tradition. It is unfortunate to record that Lord Bacon was an unsuccessful, but enthusiastic, experimenter himself. He is reported to have died of bronchitis contracted while stuffing dead poultry with snow in an effort to observe the effects of refrigeration on the preservation of flesh. Bacon's great work on the philosophy of science, *Novum Organum* (meaning the new instrument of learning—induction), led to the triumphs of Newton, Hooke, Boyle, and other English experimenters of the succeeding age.

1.2.2   Renaissance Science

The scientific triumphs of Sir Isaac Newton (1642–1727) stimulated immense popular interest in physics and mathematics, and many science writers appeared who endeavored to explain the new concepts, such as gravity and momentum, to the public. (Science writers can be described as journalists who explain the findings of science to the public; they are not to be confused with scientific writers, who are scientists writing for other scientists.)

At the same time, English literary style was characterized by great ornateness and rhetoric in usage. Perhaps in reaction to such excesses, it became the goal of scientific and technical writers of the period to write as simply and plainly as possible, a goal which is not easy to attain.

Thomas Sprat, in his *History of the Royal Society*, wrote in 1667 that the aim of society members was to return to

> . . . primitive purity, and shortness, when men delivered so many things, almost in an equal number of words. They have exacted from all their members a close, naked, natural way of speaking; positive expressions; clear senses; a native easiness: bringing all things as near the Mathematical plainness as they can: and preferring the language of Artizans, Countrymen, and Merchants, before that of Wits, or Scholars.

Sprat's "primitive purity and shortness" still do not make for easy reading. The development of a fluent, clear English prose style remained a task for Dryden and later writers.

1.2.3   Modern Prose Sources

John Dryden (1631–1700), notable not as a scientist but as a poet and critic, is credited by many scholars with shaping English prose into its present variety and serviceability. English prose written before Dryden tends to sound long-winded, or stilted, or rigid and ungraceful to the modern reader. Dryden was the first to thoroughly explore all the capabilities of prose style. In particular, he developed a flowing, informal manner of statement. This easy style, as cultivated even more fully by Joseph Addison (1672–1719), is similar to the graceful style of such present magazines as *The New Yorker*, which can be studied with profit by any modern writer. To summarize, it can be said of Dryden that good English prose written since his time tends to sound modern; that written before his time often sounds old-fashioned.

If Dryden can be acclaimed for stabilizing English prose style, then Dr. Samuel Johnson (1709–1784) can be acclaimed for

10

stabilizing punctuation, spelling, and usage. That such stabilization was needed can be deduced from the foregoing excerpt from Sprat. Dr. Johnson (the subject of Boswell's great biography, *The Life of Johnson*) singlehandedly wrote the first major English dictionary. So great was his scholarship and authority that words have been spelled and used with reasonable consistency in sentences ever since. Dr. Johnson was noted for his irascibility and wit, and some of his definitions are still famous for these qualities. For instance, because Johnson affected to detest the Scottish people, he defined the word *oats* as "A grain which in England is generally given to horses, but in Scotland supports the people."

1.2.4   Popular Science Tradition

Following Dr. Johnson, a long line of noteworthy scientific writers graced English history. Popular interest in science was renewed most largely perhaps by Charles Darwin (1809–1882), whose theory of evolution seemed to discredit Christian accounts of the genesis of man. Darwin and a contemporary, Alfred Wallace, together wrote extensively of the geology, biology, and paleontology of evolution. However, it was a disciple of Darwin's, T. H. Huxley (1825–1895), sometimes called "Darwin's bulldog" because of his sideburns and jowly appearance, who brought the proofs of evolution home most closely and vigorously to the layman. Huxley is famous for his efforts to carry the findings of science down to the lowest educational level (as if eminent scientists of today were to lecture to labor union members). In this he continued the tradition of the Royal Society of London, which has always been that of public demonstration and public lecture.

Huxley's famous lecture on chalk, which was given to an audience of workingmen, begins with analysis of the chemicals in a piece of chalk, proceeds to examine the floor of the ocean, and continues on to discuss life and evolution. The debt of prose to Dryden is clear in this lecture. Here is a portion of it:

If the sea were drained off, you might drive a wagon all the way from Valentia, on the west coast of Ireland, to Trinity Bay, in Newfoundland. And, except upon one sharp incline about two hundred miles from Valentia, I am not quite sure that it would even be necessary to put the skid on, so gentle are the ascents and descents upon that long route. From Valentia the road would lie downhill for about two hundred miles to the point at which the bottom is now covered by seventeen hundred fathoms of sea water. Then would come the central plain, more than a thousand miles wide, the inequalities of the surface of which would be hardly perceptible, though the depth of water upon it now varies from ten thousand to fifteen thousand feet; and there are places in which Mont Blanc might be sunk without showing its peak above water. Beyond this, the ascent of the American side commences, and gradually leads, for about three hundred miles, to the Newfoundland shore.

Almost the whole of the bottom of this central plain (which extends for many hundred miles in a north and south direction) is covered by a fine mud which, when brought to the surface, dries into a grayish-white friable substance. You can write with this on a blackboard if you are so inclined; and, to the eye, it is quite like very soft, grayish chalk. Examined chemically, it proves to be composed almost wholly of carbonate of lime; and if you make a section of it in the same way as that of the piece of chalk was made, and view it with the microscope, it presents innumerable globigerinae embedded in a granular matrix. Thus this deep-sea mud is substantially chalk.*

Huxley was one of the clearest, most gifted scientists who ever undertook to explain his field. Later English writers succeeded him ably—among them Joseph Lister, James Clerk Maxwell, Lord Kelvin, J. J. Thomson, James Jeans, and Arthur Eddington. However, the emphasis in this review will now pass to American scientific and technical writers, the English traditions having been thoroughly established and brilliantly supported by all the men cited.

1.3   **AMERICAN SOURCES**

1.3.1   **Early American Science**

Various names are associated with scientific and technical writing in the American Colonies and in the early American Republic. The first name which comes to mention here is Cotton Mather (1663–1728), a Puritan minister whose chief distinction perhaps is not a praiseworthy one. Mather early collected prejudiced "evi-

---

*F. R. Moulton and J. J. Schifferes, *The Autobiography of Science*, Doubleday & Company, Inc., Garden City, New York, 1960, p. 391.

dence" on the existence of witchcraft in the Colonies, and he was instrumental in getting several unfortunates convicted and hanged for this fancied crime.

Mather, however, was greatly interested in scientific progress of all sorts and collected evidence in the new settlements on many useful topics. In 1713 he had a paper, "Curiosa Americana," read before the Royal Society of London; he subsequently became the first American elected to membership. The paper contained various items of scientific interest dealing with American plants, animals, and minerals. Other communications of a similar nature followed. Some topics of most interest to Mather were smallpox inoculation, cross-pollination of plants, and distinctive American animals, such as the moose and rattlesnake. Mather cannot be considered an experimental scientist himself, but his curiosity led him to collect descriptions of certain natural phenomena, and, for this reason, he can be called a technical writer.

The part played by Benjamin Franklin (1706–1790) in American history is well known. "Poor Richard's" many inventions, his writing, and his important researches in electrical theory earn him the titles of scientist, inventor, and scientific and technical writer. For instance, Franklin is credited with proving that electricity and lightning are different manifestations of the same substance, with inventing the lightning rod, bifocal spectacles, and the Franklin stove, and with founding the first American scientific group (the American Philosophical Society).

Franklin wrote voluminously on a hundred topics. He is, for instance, the author of a well-known letter to a young man which lists all the considerations of importance in taking a mistress. A more modest passage on constructing a kite and drawing lightning down along the string is recommended. Note the practical American concern with apparatus rather than with theory (in the last line).

> To the top of the upright stick of the cross is to be fixed a very sharp-pointed wire, rising a foot or more above the wood. To the end of the twine, next to the hand, is to be tied a silk ribbon, and where the silk and twine join, a key may be fastened. This kite is to be raised when a thunder-gust appears to be coming on, and the person who holds the string must stand within a door or window or under some cover, so that the silk ribbon may not be wet; and

care must be taken that the twine does not touch the frame of the door or window. As soon as any of the thunder-clouds come over the kite, the pointed wire will draw the electric fire from them, and the kite, with all the twine, will be electrified, and the loose filaments of the twine will stand out every way, and be attracted by an approaching finger. And when the rain has wet the kite and twine, so that it can conduct the electric fire freely, you will find it stream out plentifully from the key on the approach of your knuckle. At this key the phial may be charged; and from electric fire thus obtained, spirits may be kindled, and all the other electric experiments be performed, which are usually done by the help of a rubbed glass globe or tube, and thereby the sameness of the electric matter with that of lightning completely demonstrated.*

1.3.2   Nineteenth Century Science

One American whose name is attached to a unit of physical measurement is Joseph Henry (1797–1878), after whom the unit of electrical inductance, the henry, is named. Henry's work resulted in part in the invention of the telegraph by Samuel Morse, who gave divine power all the credit in the famous phrase "What hath God wrought!"

Henry describes his observations on induction in workmanlike prose in the following passage. Note again the concern with apparatus rather than theory.

When a small battery is moderately excited by diluted acid, and its poles, which should be terminated by cups of mercury, are connected by a copper wire not more than a foot in length, no spark is perceived when the connection is either formed or broken; but if a wire thirty or forty feet long be used instead of the short wire, though no spark will be perceptible when the connection is made, yet when it is broken by drawing one end of the wire from its cup of mercury, a vivid spark is produced. If the action of the battery be very intense, a spark will be given by the short wire; in this case it is only necessary to wait a few minutes until the action partially subsides, and until no more sparks are given from the short wire; if the long wire be now substituted a spark will again be obtained. The effect appears somewhat increased by coiling the wire into a helix; it seems also to depend in some measure on the length and thickness of the wire.

I can account for these phenomena only by supposing the long

*Ibid., p. 236.

wire to become charged with electricity, which by its reaction on itself projects a spark when the connection is broken.*

In the period after Henry, scientific researches of greatest interest were perhaps those in medicine. In this period, Oliver Wendell Holmes (1809–1894), physician and author, wrote on childbed fever, and anesthetics were discovered by Crawford Long and William Morton.

A great American physicist conducted classical researches on thermodynamics at Yale University a little later. Willard Gibbs (1839–1903) has not been credited in popular literature for the extent and depth of his work in physical chemistry, but scientists in England and Germany have honored him for a century. The subtlety and complexity of his thought can be noted in the following passage on thermodynamics:

> It is an inference naturally suggested by the general increase of entropy which accompanies the changes occurring in any isolated material system that when the entropy of the system has reached a maximum the system will be in a state of equilibrium. Although this principle has by no means escaped the attention of physicists, its importance does not appear to have been duly appreciated. Little has been done to develop the principle as a foundation for the general theory of thermodynamic equilibrium.
>
> The principle may be formulated as follows, constituting a criterion of equilibrium:
>
> 1. For the equilibrium of any isolated system it is necessary and sufficient that in all possible variations of the state of the system which do not alter its energy, the variation of its entropy shall either vanish or be negative.
>
> The following form, which is easily shown to be equivalent to the preceding, is often more convenient in application:
>
> 2. For the equilibrium of any isolated system it is necessary and sufficient that in all possible variations of the state of the system which do not alter its entropy, the variation of its energy shall either vanish or be positive.†

Gibbs' writing seems modern in comparison with Henry's (Henry preceded him by about forty years). This is because

*Ibid., p. 292.
†Ibid., pp. 466–467.

Gibbs' thought was complex and mathematical, not necessarily because Gibbs was a better writer. Indeed, Gibbs here exhibits some of the defects of modern writing; for example, unnecessarily long sentences bare of such concrete references as the wires and sparks of Henry or the kites and keys of Franklin. It is always clearer to discuss objects than it is to discuss ideas, and objects should be included when possible.

1.3.3   Aerodynamics, Missiles, and Space Flight

A scientist and writer who analyzed and discussed a modern object is Samuel P. Langley (1834–1906). Langley, an astronomer and a pioneer aerodynamicist, built an airplane (in 1896) before the Wright brothers. Though the unmanned craft flew only a half mile, it must be counted a success. Langley put into it more flight theory than any other man of the time possessed. From this early triumph, Langley went on to design a steam-driven, manned aircraft. The craft, however, proved to be underpowered and crashed into the Potomac. This ambitious undertaking, having a fate similar to that of America's early spacecraft, was dubbed "Langley's folly." A short time after, the Wright brothers completed their successful flight and received all the accolades. However, Glenn Curtiss later installed a more powerful engine in an aircraft of Langley's design and flew it, proving Langley's aerodynamic theories.

In the passage which follows, Langley discusses some of his early flight studies. Aerodynamics was indeed in its infancy, and his research had to begin with bird flight. Most reputable scientists of the day regarded airplane flight as a subject for crackpots, just as space flight was regarded in 1950. Unfortunately the passage is marred by one excessively long sentence.

In all discussions of flight, especially of soaring flight, the first source to which one naturally looks for information is birds. But here correct deductions from even the most accurate of observations are very difficult, because the observation cannot include all of the conditions under which the bird is doing its work. If we could but see the wind, the problem would be greatly simplified, but as the matter stands, it may be said that much less assistance has been derived from studious observations on bird flight than might have been anticipated, perhaps because it has been found thus far impos-

16

sible to reproduce in the flying machine or aerostatic model the shape and condition of wing with its flexible and controllable connection with the body, and especially the instinctive control of the wing to meet the requirements of flight that are varying from second to second, and which no automatic adjustment can adequately meet.*

A modern American space scientist will complete the tally of experts quoted in this chapter. The scientist is John R. Pierce of the Bell Telephone Laboratories. Pierce is credited with presenting the first engineering systems analysis of communications satellites, and he was instrumental in the design of the Echo and Telstar satellites. In addition, he has to his credit many inventions dealing with amplifiers. He is also the inventor of the electron gun, or Pierce gun.

The passage which follows is quoted from an article Pierce published in the *Scientific American*. The article discusses the transmission and reception of radio signals by a satellite. Note the workmanlike style of the article, both as it explains ideas and as it describes components. This balance of the theoretical and the practical, difficult to achieve, is invaluable to any reader to whom the ideas are new. Other points of style worthy of note are the short sentences (not always easy to write), the many logical signposts furnished by words such as *because, however, but,* and *hence,* and the imaginative use of comparisons and examples. In this style, Gibbs and Henry are at last united.

Because it is costly to put weight in orbit, satellite transmitters must be kept low in power. The weight of electronic circuitry itself is negligible. The chief source of weight is the power supply: solar cells and storage batteries. (Nuclear power sources may eventually offer weight savings, but this remains to be shown.) In designing an economic satellite communication system, therefore, one must use the lowest power consonant with highly reliable service. This power is determined not only by the sensitivity of receivers but also by the strength of competing signals—that is, by noise.

In evaluating the effects of noise we need some scale of measurement. A convenient scale is one based on the electromagnetic radiation emitted by hot objects. For example, the filament of an incandescent lamp glowing at a temperature of a few thousand degrees Kelvin (degrees centigrade above absolute zero) produces about the same amount of noise as that added to the signal by a

*Ibid., p. 472.

good microwave receiver of 1950 design. Since then maser amplifiers have been developed with a noise level so low that it corresponds to a temperature of only about 10 degrees Kelvin. Hence, it is now possible to detect signals that would have been hopelessly drowned in the noise produced by receivers of 10 years ago.*

Scientific and technical writing probably did not come of age in the United States until the period which Pierce discusses, the 1950's. In England a tradition of great science and of great men writing was established early and long maintained, principally by members of the Royal Society of London.

Science in the United States before World War II was the province of a few brilliant men whose misfortune it was to work in comparative solitude: men such as Gibbs, Langley, and Goddard, the father of liquid rocketry. However, much was changed by the war. Public interest in applied science increased enormously and technical writing became a profession. The events which led to this change were the wartime interest in nuclear energy and radar and the heavy expenditure of public funds to develop the required technology.

The Manhattan Project was credited with the design of nuclear explosives. This secret project, however, was little known to the public until after the war, and it did not have the immediate influence which radar projects had. Radar, communications, and control systems design performed in American and Allied laboratories was reported in the *Massachusetts Institute of Technology Radiation Laboratory Series* (McGraw-Hill), a series of twenty-eight volumes on electronics, servo, and high-frequency radiation techniques. This series of textbooks probably represents the first significantly large body of technical writing in the nation's history.

Following World War II, technical writing prospered as a profession. This prosperity was created by government funding of large development contracts for guided missiles, radar and armament control systems, inertial navigation systems, flight control systems, experimental aircraft, computers, nuclear explosives, and so on. Many of these developments are now a part of the nation's history. The names of some of the missiles, for instance, make a spectacular roster: Snark, Navaho, Atlas, Jupiter, Thor, Redstone,

---

*By permission from John R. Pierce, "Communication Satellites," *Scientific American*, Oct., 1961, pp. 94–95.

Corporal, Pershing, Honest John, Davy Crockett, Terrier, Talos, Falcon, Sidewinder, Minuteman, and Titan.

The emphasis in technical development is now on the peaceful vehicles of space, such as Mercury, Gemini, Apollo, Tiros, Voyager, Telstar, and Mariner. Possibly, scientific and technical writing will next record man's conquest of the solar system, as it has recorded his conquest of the land and the air.

2 Qualitative Aspects

It was suggested in Chapter 1 that the purpose of the writer of fiction is to make the reader undergo an experience; that is, participate vicariously in some entertaining or dramatic situation. Only after the reader has undergone the emotions which the author shapes does he begin to think consciously about them.

The purpose of the factual writer, on the other hand, is to convey truths or opinions about the world directly, without intervention of the emotions.

Both writers, however, must possess five qualities of writing technique before they can be effective. These qualities are, in the sequence in which they will be examined, as follows: (1) knowledge of the subject, (2) knowledge of the audience, (3) effective organization of material, (4) effective writing style, and (5) motivation in writing.

A geometrical model of the writing process involving these five items is suggested in the block diagram. It is assumed that some pattern of relations exists in space and time which the writer understands and which he wishes to convey to the reader's mind. This process is carried out with the aid of various intermediate "filters" (items 1 through 4) which appear in the sketch. Each filter has the useful effect of reducing the dimensionality of the material it acts upon by selecting some significant profile of the material. The

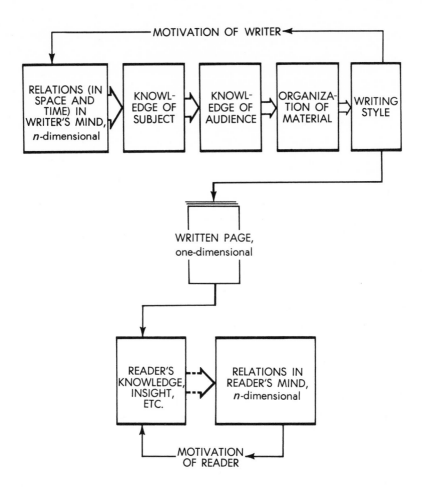

motivation which keeps the words flowing in the two loops is supplied by the two motivation "batteries." The reading process, accomplished by a scanning of the page, can restore the dimensionality which is lost by translation of the original material into the unidimensional flow of words. Thus the reader must supply knowledge and insight of his own. This will be discussed at more length later in this chapter.

It is interesting to note that the filters in the writing process are foreshadowed in a well-known quotation from Francis Bacon, perhaps the first major English scientific writer: "Reading maketh a full man, conference a ready man, and writing an exact man."

Although it stretches Bacon's original meaning somewhat, we can say of technical writing that reading gives knowledge of the subject, conference gives knowledge of the audience, and writing gives practice in style and organization.

2.1   KNOWLEDGE OF SUBJECT

The writer, ideally, should be fully charged with his subject. It should overflow his brain to such an extent that ideas crowd in and beg for expression. But these clamorous ideas must be formed in ranks which are perfectly disciplined by the writer before they are sent on parade. They must march forth regularly and logically in a sort of crisp military review. One stumble and the whole display is marred.

An example of such a crisp presentation can be supplied by Ernest Hemingway; the subject is trout fishing (from *In Our Time*). The author's purpose is to make the reader experience all the fine emotions of trout fishing. He does this so straightforwardly and modestly that the passage can also be taken as a skillful model of technical writing.

> [Nick] started down to the stream, holding his rod, the bottle of grasshoppers hung from his neck by a thong tied in half hitches around the neck of the bottle. . . .
>
> Rushing, the current sucked against his legs. Where he stepped in, the water was over his knees. He waded with the current. The gravel slid under his shoes. He looked down at the swirl of water below each leg and tipped up the bottle to get a grasshopper.
>
> The first grasshopper gave a jump in the neck of the bottle and went out into the water. He was sucked under in the whirl by Nick's right leg and came to the surface a little way down stream. He floated rapidly, kicking. In a quick circle, breaking the surface of the water, he disappeared. A trout had taken him.
>
> Another hopper poked his head out of the bottle. His antennae wavered. He was getting his front legs out of the bottle to jump. Nick took him by the head and held him while he threaded the slim hook under his chin, down through his thorax and into the last segments of his abdomen. The grasshopper took hold of the hook with his front feet, spitting tobacco juice on it. Nick dropped him into the water. . . .
>
> There was a tug on the line. Nick pulled against the taut line. It was his first strike. Holding the now living rod across the cur-

rent, he brought in the line with his left hand. The rod bent in jerks, the trout pumping against the current. . . .

Nick took the line in his left hand and pulled the trout, thumping tiredly against the current, to the surface. His back was mottled the clear, water-over-gravel color, his side flashing in the sun. The rod under his arm, Nick stooped, dipping his right hand into the current. He held the trout, never still, with his moist right hand, while he unhooked the barb from his mouth, then dropped him back into the stream.

He hung unsteadily in the current, then settled to the bottom beside a stone. Nick reached down his hand to touch him, his arm to the elbow under water. The trout was steady in the moving stream, resting on the gravel, beside a stone. As Nick's fingers touched him, touched his smooth, cool, underwater feeling he was gone, gone in a shadow across the bottom of the stream. . . .

He had wet his hand before he touched the trout, so he would not disturb the delicate mucus that covered him. If a trout was touched with a dry hand, a white fungus attacked the unprotected spot. Years before when he had fished crowded streams, with fly fishermen ahead of him and behind him, Nick had again and again come on dead trout, furry with white fungus, drifted against a rock, or floating belly up in some pool.*

Note in this passage the great knowledge of his subject which Hemingway possesses. This knowledge is so nearly complete and instant that we are ready to believe that everything he wrote actually occurred. In fact, we are persuaded that he wrote from memory, without any of the sweat of scholarship. Thus he captures our belief at once, as all readers must be captured if they are to participate in recreating the subject matter from the words.

Research and notes, of course, are needed in any writing project, but, ideally, this material should be so fused with the writer's intimate knowledge that no seam or joint is visible in the union. This requires that the experience, the scholarship, and the thought precede the act of writing. The moment of setting pen to paper should be charged with electricity.

The passage quoted can be examined profitably for other examples of writing technique. Hemingway's purpose, as noted, is to make the reader participate. He does this in the first place by

---

*By permission from Ernest Hemingway, "Big Two-hearted River," In Our Time, Charles Scribner's Sons, New York, © 1925, 1930, p. 199.

capturing the reader's belief with his superior knowledge, like a hypnotist. He does this in the second place by tricking the reader into remembering similar impressions of his own. Note the many vivid phrases relating to seeing, sensing, touching, and the like: "His back was mottled the clear, water-over-gravel color...," "...touched his smooth, cool underwater feeling...," "The rod bent in jerks, the trout pumping against the current...," or "...dead trout, furry with white fungus...."

Hemingway's style is notable for other elements, such as clarity, brevity, and color—aspects of style which will be examined in succeeding sections. It is his mastery of subject matter which is emphasized here, and it is this which shapes his style. Knowledge of subject is the first requisite, then, for successful writing.

2.2 KNOWLEDGE OF AUDIENCE

Knowledge of the audience is more important for some writers than for others. A great poet or novelist probably constitutes his own audience in the sense that he writes to satisfy the canons of his own taste, without regard for others. The audience must accept him on his own terms. The technical writer cannot be so dictatorial. All his articles, all his reports are written for a special audience. However, he need not challenge or stimulate his audience. They usually come to him eager for any sort of information on his topic. They are willing to read to understand—not criticize.

A remarkably successful technical writer, one whose success may be due largely to an intimate knowledge of his audience, is Dr. Benjamin Spock, authority on child care. As you read the following selection, note how Dr. Spock gains the trust of his specialized audience, then builds up their confidence. The first passage quoted is about an infant.

> "I'm so afraid I'll hurt him if I don't handle him right," a mother often says about her first baby. You don't have to worry, you have a pretty tough baby. There are many ways to hold him. If his head drops backward by mistake it won't hurt him. The open spot in his skull (the fontanel) is covered by a tough membrane like canvas that isn't easily injured. The system to control his body temperature is working quite well by the time he weighs 7 pounds if he's covered halfway sensibly. He has a good resistance to most germs. During a family cold epidemic he's apt to have it the mildest

of all. If he gets his head tangled in anything he has a strong instinct to struggle and yell. If he's not getting enough to eat, he will probably cry for more. If the light is too strong for his eyes, he'll blink and fuss. (You can take his picture with a flash bulb, even if it does make him jump.) He knows how much sleep he needs and takes it. He can care for himself pretty well for a person who can't say a word and knows nothing about the world.*

In considering the above passage, note how Dr. Spock handles a difficult technical problem. In the first place, he has an extremely complex, nonstandardized "mechanism"—a baby—to describe. He knows this subject as well as possible, but he also recognizes that much is unknown about babies. As far as the audience is concerned, Dr. Spock is aware of the fact that parents have successfully raised children for thousands of years and that the parents' own loving instincts are often the best guide. This audience includes readers, mostly women, of all educational levels, ranging from grammar school to graduate school. This audience, moreover, usually opens the book under trying circumstances, often with a crying baby or an ill baby at hand.

Considering these customer-specifications, then, what dispositions of style and subject matter have been made? In the first place, Dr. Spock continually reassures the reader that his own judgment is valid in emergencies. Dr. Spock also qualifies his statements in many ways—this, of course, because babies are not standardized. Each one must be treated as a "development model." There are many phrases which suggest this caution; for example, "At the other extreme," "Sometimes he will not do what is expected," "Now I had better turn around and say that . . ." The passage quoted is not an example of good technical writing, because the text is too highly qualified; but the reasons for this caution are, of course, excellent.

To make sure his variously educated audiences understand him, Dr. Spock employs a chatty, conversational writing style, rather like a physician's bedside manner. This gives the impression that he is nearby, offering calm counsel. Notice the highly flexible use of the personal pronouns *I*, *you*, and *he*. This informal dealing

*By permission from Benjamin Spock, M.D., *Pocket Book of Baby and Child Care*, Pocket Books, Inc., New York, 1951, © 1945, 1946, by Benjamin Spock, p. 20.

with his subjects makes for a very simple sentence structure. Introduction of his actors in this manner is always highly useful to a writer, as will be discussed at more length later when style is considered.

2.3   ORGANIZATION OF MATERIAL

To know a subject well is to have the material already organized and pigeonholed somehow in one's mind. The problem of the writer, then, is to translate his existing mental organization into a verbal organization. This task is especially difficult because it requires that the multidimensional brain pattern — comprehending space, time, electric charge, magnetic field, etc. — be reduced to a one-dimensional flow of words on the written page.

The mathematician will recognize that a true translation of this sort is not possible: one dimension is not adequate. The writer can present on paper only a profile of what he knows. This profile, however, if skillfully depicted in words, can be recreated into a full-blown image by an imaginative, attentive reader. The translating process thus requires skill, knowledge, and good judgment on the part of both reader and writer. It is all rather like the art of the sketcher who, viewing a head, reduces all its lines and planes and masses, with a few simple strokes, to a line drawing. Some artistic sense enables him to select from all he sees the few quick lines, perhaps as few as twenty or thirty, which suggest most aptly the subject's appearance and character. The viewer perceives this suggestive likeness and is satisfied, remarking that the simple pattern "looks just like him."

The quality which is being considered here is the quality of selection. This is the ability to perceive fundamental details and array them quickly and clearly on paper. All writing, like all sketching, requires selection, then. Selection, moreover, requires thought, experience, self-criticism, and the exercise of good taste.

A general rule for effective organization of written material is this: Organize words to obey the logic of organization which the subject itself possesses. In other words, parallel objective structure somehow with verbal structure.

When the subject being described is related to time, a simple chronological organization can be used. Chronological organization can be employed for historical matter or in recording the flow of actual events. The events described on paper follow the sequential flow which occurred in time. This is the organizing principle which Hemingway employed in describing trout fishing.

When more general subjects are discussed, a more general organization must be employed. Often some unique physical principle attached to the subject can be conveniently used. A radar set, for instance, can fix the position of distant objects in space. To do this it generates pulses of electromagnetic energy which are transmitted through space, reflected, and then detected as echoes. A description of a radar set might be organized under the principal headings of *Pulse Generation, Pulse Transmission, Pulse Detection,* and *Pulse Display.* All less important topics, such as power supply, transmitting and receiving antennas, tuning circuit, and voltage regulator, can be treated as subheadings. These secondary elements are necessary to the operation of the radar, of course, but they are not used exclusively in radar sets. They are only auxiliary components in a radar set and should be so treated. The key principle of organization, then, is to detect some natural sequence in the material being considered, whether it is a time sequence, a signal flow sequence, or a formal logical sequence, and to base the outline on this natural sequence.

Most long technical reports actually follow a combination of sequences. Consider the organization of *Baby and Child Care.* Dr. Spock may again be quoted to good effect.

> There are four things that I want to explain before you start reading. The topics are arranged to correspond to your baby's age. You can read along bit by bit, as he grows older, and find answers to the questions that naturally come up. You don't have to read the whole book ahead of time. Thumb-sucking, for instance, is taken up early, because most babies who ever suck their thumbs try to do it before they are 3 months old. But when I get started telling you about thumb-sucking, I want also to tell you about it in the older child, so that the subject won't be chopped up into little pieces in different parts of the book. Toward the end of the book are the topics like measles and first aid that don't belong to any one age period. When your child gets spots or a burn, you'll expect to look it up in the Index anyway. Use the Index at the back when you

are troubled. It's arranged to help you find the answers. Under "Stomach-ache" it will tell you all the places in the book where stomach-ache is mentioned.*

Dr. Spock's book is thus organized on what might be called a *chronological-topical* basis. The verbal organization parallels the physical development of a baby in time, but once a topic is introduced it is completely discussed for all age levels before another topic is taken up.

A final warning concerning the organization of material: Overwriting and underwriting must be considered poor organizing practices. The beginner usually overwrites when he tries to tell everything he knows, without regard for relevancy. This bad habit may signify that the writer is desperate for good material, that he is showing off, or that he has tunnel vision.

Underwriting, on the other hand, may occur when insufficient research has been done. It also may occur when the writer understands his subject perfectly but does not perfectly understand himself. He does not understand, that is, that certain key links in the argument which are obvious to himself (and therefore not included) may be unknown to others. He would not draw a man with one leg gone, yet he offers an explanation with the knee and and torso gone. That the knee and torso are "obvious" does not, of course, relieve the strangeness of his handiwork. His audience is universally baffled.

Report organization is discussed in detail in Chapter 8. The basic principle should be kept in mind, however: Let verbal structure parallel the structural organizing sequences of the subject itself.

2.4   EFFECTIVE WRITING STYLE

Most authorities agree on two, and probably three, qualities which define a good technical writing style. *Clarity* and *brevity* are usually named, and often *variety* (or a like quality such as *color*). Since the purpose of technical writing is to communicate technical information, clarity is a requisite. No information can be conveyed if misunderstanding occurs; indeed, misunderstanding may bring about a dangerous situation entirely opposite to that which is desired.

Ibid., p. 1.

Brevity usually measures the efficiency of verbal transmission (once clarity is established). Clearly brevity, or efficiency, is a useful concept in measuring both the cost or labor of transmission and the labor performed by the reader.

Variety in style is useful in gaining reader cooperation and acceptance (a necessary requirement in writing proposals and brochures), but variety should be used at all times in good taste. Vulgarisms and slang usually irritate the reader.

Students of the mathematics of information theory will perceive that *clarity* can be defined as the absence of noise in the transmission circuit, and *brevity*, as the lack of redundancy. (Redundancy, of course, may sometimes be useful.) *Variety* is probably not subject to mathematical definition; it has a psychological meaning and consequently is more difficult to evaluate.

A good technical writing style will now be defined as a style possessing clarity, brevity, and variety. Hemingway's style, if evaluated in this light, possesses all these useful qualities. His presentation of information on trout fishing is clear, briefly accomplished, and full of variety.

Dr. Spock's information on baby care is also clearly presented. The brevity of his presentation, on the other hand, is not so marked as Hemingway's. There is more repetition, more substitution of phrases where a word could settle matters. And there is not so much variety; there are not many impressions of sense and color or striking metaphors, which have the effect of carrying the reader along from sentence to sentence, so that he "cannot put the book down." This is not to say that Dr. Spock has not written a highly literate book; it is only to say that he has not the literary skill of Hemingway. His purpose is also different. He intends to write in the chatty style of informal speech because he wishes to calm the worried mother.

Good style in technical writing, then, can be said to promote writing effectiveness. It is true that people often speak of style as that quality of writing by which a man expresses his personality, as he expresses it, for instance, by his style of dress. This larger definition of style, unfortunately, is not appropriate for the technical writer, who must not allow his personality to intrude prominently in his reports. This restriction may be the reason why "a common grayness silvers all" of technical writing. It might be more charitable to suggest that color in style must be sacrificed to gain precision of statement.

The unskilled writer often asks how he can develop an effective style. The best answer seems to be independent study of great authors of all sorts. Dr. Johnson, the great English lexicographer, was asked this question and replied, "Whoever wishes to attain an English style, familiar but not coarse, and elegant but not ostentatious, must give his days and nights to the volumes of Addison."

Dr. Johnson suggests that the reader study a great writer of the time, Addison, whose ease and pleasantness of style were well known. To bring this passage up to date, it is suggested here that the reader study such modern writers as Hemingway, John Pierce, and John O'Hara, all of whom write with a crisp, easy style. Certain magazines can also be studied with profit, such as *The New Yorker, Fortune, The Atlantic Monthly,* and *Scientific American.* The amateur writer who confines his reading to the daily papers and news magazines will find it difficult to develop an effective technical writing style. This results because technical writing is not a form of journalism. The depth and complexity of explanation required in technical reports transcend that required in journalism.

The reader is also warned that he should not confine his reading and study to commercial or governmental technical reports. The sins and shortcomings of some "federal prose" or "gobbledygook" are well known. One famous definition appears in the book *Federal Prose*:

> Federal prose is that form of nonmetrical composition, apparently English, which can be invariably interpreted as meaning and/or not meaning more and/or less than, rather than what, it seems to mean.*

Federal prose, as defined here, represents the attempt of the ill-educated person to clothe himself in worn-out, patched phrases cast off originally by more imaginative authors who knew when to discard them.

The last suggestion for developing a good style is to write and rewrite constantly. Only in this manner can skill and ease with words be developed. One superlative author, Leo Tolstoy, is said to have rewritten some passages of his novels as many as ten times

---

*J. R. Masterson and W. B. Phillips, *Federal Prose*, The University of North Carolina Press, Chapel Hill, 1948, p. 25.

before yielding them up to his editors. The unskilled writer surely cannot afford less than his most devoted effort.

MOTIVATION IN WRITING

Dr. Johnson, author of the famous English dictionary, has discussed motivation in writing. His most famous statement is a pithy one: "No man but a blockhead ever wrote except for money." But this admirable advice may be beside the point. What quality of mind is it that sends an author's words gushing from his pen in a sort of running, black fountain? It is probably more than the promise of money. Dr. Johnson is quoted in another interesting statement: "Tom Birch is as brisk as a bee in conversation; but no sooner does he take a pen in hand, than it becomes a torpedo to him, and benumbs all his faculties."

What is it that torpedoes a writer's faculties, then, we might inquire. The torpedo may lie deep in a writer's personality. It may lie in a guilty perfectionism which requires that his first paragraph be a model for all the future. Consequently the first paragraph is endlessly reworked and mauled but never completed.

The torpedo may be a distaste for writing, engendered in grade school when the act of writing was associated with a forbidding, threatening teacher and tedious rules whose use was never justified. Or it may be a writer's fear of self-betrayal—a taking of the Fifth Amendment, so to speak, by refusing to place on record his beliefs and opinions.

Of more immediate concern, however, are two additional torpedoes that benumb a writer's faculties. One of them (Torpedo A) is lack of ease with words and rules of grammar, and the other (Torpedo B) is simply a lack of enthusiasm for the task of writing.

Torpedo A can be disarmed by the study and practice of writing. Those writers who are favored with natural talent will learn easily, but, even so, they will profit by work. Other writers may be comforted by the fact that serviceable technical writing can be turned out by any normal individual who applies common sense and patience to the task. Technical writing is easier than literary writing, because it does not require the cultivation of a mood and is more responsive to logical planning.

Torpedo B can be disarmed by the cultivation of interest in a

Qualitative Aspects   31

topic. It is strange that many authors need the stimulation of enthusiasm before they can function properly. Enthusiasm is not required in adding a column of numbers or in applying the binomial theorem, but, in writing about even an automobile starter, it can be useful in dissolving the raw edges of refractory ideas and making them flow into some sort of coherence.

How this enthusiasm can be achieved is a personal matter. Coffee, liquor, and drugs have all been applied, but knowledge of the subject may be even more useful.

3   *Characteristics of Language*

This chapter discusses the nature of the English language and compares it with other communication media, insofar as this can be done in a brief, descriptive manner. The fundamental topics discussed in this chapter include the relation of English to various symbolic languages, computer manipulation of language, information theory, symbolic logic, the origins of language and of writing, the formation of word groups, definition, indexing and abstracting, semantics, and word classification. All these topics are in the air at present and provoke many questions in writing courses. Some of these questions will be answered in this chapter.

None of the traditional rules of English grammar will be presented in this chapter. Instead, these will be codified and presented in two appendixes, to which anyone who has forgotten his high school or college terminology can quickly turn for refreshment. Appendix A presents definitions of grammatical terminology, and Appendix B presents word and word group structural "trees."

These defining trees will prove especially suitable for the engineer, who is used to viewing diagrams whenever such a geometric codification is available.

3.1   LANGUAGE AND COMMUNICATION

3.1.1   Language and Mathematics

The engineer is tempted to think of words as being akin, somehow, to numbers and of sentences as being akin to equations. Thus he attempts to construct parallels between writing and algebra, a largely fruitless practice. It is true that all equations can be stated in terms of sentences, but it is not true that all sentences can be stated in terms of equations. The verbal language is far more flexible in its applications than the mathematical language.

We can translate the equation $ax + bx^2 = k$ into words, for instance, as "The quantity a times x plus the quantity b times x *squared* is equal to k." But we cannot use equations to tell some friend that "the house next door is burning with fierce orange flames and black smoke." We could possibly recite formulas for the burning rates of wood and carpets, and supply some large coefficients for evaluation of, say, q (for heat evolved) and r (for radiation evolved). But this would be entirely inadequate, because equations can only represent quantitative and logical relationships. Instead, we need the quick reporting of certain temporary facts and emotional impressions before our own furniture is consumed.

Further examination of the rich stores of information that can be conveyed with language—from *I love you* to *Get lost!*—will show that language is the most varied of all our schemes of communication, though certainly not the most exact. *Get lost!* and *I love you* actually mean nothing in terms of concrete detail, and different people interpret these sentences in entirely different ways.

The English language, to be made exact, requires a closely controlled, common set of definitions for writer and reader, and this control is possible only among persons closely related in research or engineering. When such control is exercised, the language tends to gain precision, exactness, and penetration and tends to lose variety and flexibility. Scientific usage tends, moreover, to substitute symbols for words and phrases in order to make definition exact and manipulation convenient.

Mathematics, which was once stated entirely in words, has in perhaps little more than two thousand years changed into a symbolic (as opposed to a verbal) form of communication. But it is not the only symbolic form of communication. Highway road signs are largely symbolic, depicting as they do a sharp curve or a dangerous crossing without the aid of letters. A more extensive symbolic language is that used in electrical circuit schematics. Diodes, batteries, antennas, leads, junctions, capacitors, resistors, and many other elements are represented conventionally by carefully defined symbols. The battery, for instance, looks like ⊣ ⊢ and the resistor like ⎓⋀⋀⎓ .

3.1.2   Language and Memory

All forms of communication require a common set of experiences, or a *shared memory* between transmitter and receiver. The greater the number of similar college courses engineers have taken, for instance, the better they can communicate. And the more detailed the coding in the instrumentation channel between a space ship and an earth tracking station, the more the space ship can tell the station about such heavenly matters as solar wind drifts, Van Allen belt intensities, dust particle frequencies, and the solar ultraviolet spectrum.

That there is an absolute requirement in all communication for a shared memory was pointed up in a series of attempts scientists made to communicate with the inhabitants of other planets. The communications carrier was not difficult to devise: high-frequency radio transmission directed at the other planet. But what was to be the form of message and coding? It was finally concluded that the message could relate only to information presumably shared by both sending and receiving planets, and that the most suitable choice was elementary mathematical information. It was possible, in other words, for such utter strangers to say only something like "Two pulses and two pulses make four pulses" (though this was not, in fact, an actual message).

Communication in terms of words requires a far more elaborate shared memory than any other form. Indeed, almost every human experience we have had since birth may shape in some way our understanding of a complex document.

Characteristics of Language   35

3.1.3 Language and Information Theory

Information theory is a form of applied mathematics dealing with electrical and electromechanical communication systems. Acquaintance with information theory is highly useful for the communications engineer who must deal with electrically coded signals in radios, radars, television sets, computers, servos, and elementary human nerve networks. But the exact manner in which the human brain operates to produce an intelligible sentence cannot yet be specified in terms of electrical pulses, and, therefore, information theory cannot very well be applied to verbal communication.

It is true that words can be arbitrarily coded into standard communications systems in terms of voltage pulses. But information theory has nothing to tell of the "meaning" of these pulse patterns. It can only predict the probability of these patterns' getting through the transmission loop in a recognizable form. Perhaps it may show that the loop can accommodate only 10,000 pulses per second, or perhaps it may show that the receiver noise level is too high or the bandwidth too narrow for ungarbled transmission.

Information theory, in short, has nothing to do with the creation of meaning. It deals only with the probability for successful transmission when the meaning is coded in a particular manner for a particular transmission loop. This may be something like the chances for delivery of a dozen uncrushed eggs during the Christmas mailing rush. The eggs themselves would not constitute the meaning of the transmission, of course. The meaning would lie in the thought behind the gift. And this meaning would become more obscure the more the eggs were crushed.

3.1.4 Language and Symbolic Logic

Symbolic logic is closely related to mathematics and also to the forms of language we use when we reason. Indeed, symbolic logic is very useful in analyzing mathematics and language themselves. The logical processes which Euclid used when he discussed geometry and Aristotle used when he discussed logic were conducted almost entirely in terms of words. Reasoning continued to be a largely verbal process until approximately 1847, when Boole and De Morgan presented papers which, in effect, invented the algebra of logical processes.

Since that time, standardized symbols have been used for much formal mathematical reasoning. These symbols replace the logical and inferential components of language and make it possible to manipulate propositional statements in much the same manner as equations. Examples of symbolic notation are ⊃ for *if . . . then* and ~ for *not*. The two statements

1. If you are not satisfied, then we will refund your money.
2. If you marry in haste, you will repent at leisure.

are logical propositions of equivalent nature which might be stated by the same logical formula. The actual subject content of these statements is not important in symbolic logic, only the form of the argument. Most of the standard conjunctions of writing, such as *therefore, consequently, because, either,* and *or,* and many phrases, are purely logical in effect and can be replaced by specific symbols.

Symbolic logic has been extensively developed in the twentieth century, principally by Bertrand Russell (*Principia Mathematica*). In language analysis, the topics which can be examined include *meaningfulness, inference, contradiction, compatibility, relative truth,* and *redundancy.* Symbolic logic prescribes the formal sequences by which all inductive and deductive reasoning is carried out. These topics will be discussed at more length in Chapter 7.

3.1.5   Language and Computers

3.1.5.1   TRANSLATION

Anyone who has programmed a computer must have felt that he was communicating with it, though sometimes he might have been tempted to kick it for being so petty and obstinate over trifles it could very well overlook. The question arises very naturally, at any rate: Since computers process numbers in a very useful manner when they are not being petty about it, can they be set up to process words?

The answer to this question is a limited *yes.* Computers can process words if clear and explicit instructions can be provided. This, of course, includes word-for-word translation into English from foreign languages, but it does not include the ability to write original prose, nor does it necessarily include the ability to write grammatical English prose (even when translating from a

Characteristics of Language   37

grammatical foreign language). With a Russian-English vocabulary entered word for word into its memory and with the text of a Russian scientific article supplied, the computer can transpose the Russian words and type out the results in English. But the word-hash which often results may not be at all useful to the scientist who does not understand Russian idiom and figures of speech. Furthermore it may introduce genuine errors into the text—a luxury which no respectable scientist can afford.

To patch up the machine translation with extended instructions in Russian idiom and phraseology—teaching the computer to recognize Russian phrases, that is, which cannot be translated by the literal meaning of their individual words—introduces marked improvements in the translation. Still it is not now possible to completely instruct a computer in this manner. Grammar has not been well enough analyzed. Errors still persist, and the problem of translation is not considered solved.

In the long run, the Russian and English vocabularies and grammar must be completely and explicitly coded for the computer before errorless, grammatical translations can be obtained between these languages. Extensive coding of this sort does not exist for any language. Grammarians, seemingly, have been nodding in their studies for years over schemes of word classification and patterns of sentence structure which the oafish computer refuses to understand because they are descriptive rather than truly analytical. The student himself may comprehend the computer's headache when he recalls the multitudinous qualifications to almost every rule of English grammar he ever learned.

It is pleasant to report that progress is being made at some university centers in the codification of elementary grammar. Computers programmed with such a grammar can now provide acceptable translations of elementary material. When not guided by words in a foreign text, they can also compose perfectly grammatical, though random, elementary sentences. The computer might type out, for instance, "The radio smeared the ratios of several dusty carrots." This is computerized "poetry." Any human interest it might possess is supplied entirely by the human reader, not by the computer.

The random sentence actually points up a profound and little-credited rule of grammar: Proper sentence form, or sentence structure, depends not on the meaning of the words but only on their classification (*noun, verb,* etc.). In other words, the laws of syntax are independent of the laws of semantics. This conclusion is implicit in the fact that usually a wide choice exists for the manner in which we can state something. The method of statement we choose is usually determined by our personal motives, not by verbal requirements.

3.1.5.2   LANGUAGE AND ELECTRONIC DATA PROCESSING

Computers can be employed to deal with words for useful purposes other than translation. Electronic data processing (EDP) techniques are now being employed to write and print out many routine technical reports, such as parts lists and test procedures. To effect this, a catalog of possible report statements is prepared and coded. Perhaps the report can be restricted to contain combinations of only thirty basic statements, where each statement will be varied, at most, in certain minor ways. An example of such a basic statement from a test procedure is "Read and record the voltage indicated by meter number x" (x being the particular number assigned to any one of twenty possible voltmeters in the test setup). This basic statement might be cataloged as "k x."

The test engineer who writes the procedure can now instruct the reading of meter number 8 at some point in the test by simply writing "k 8," together with the step number. This instruction is presented to the computer on a punched card, along with other test instructions in their proper sequence. The computer can organize and retain all this information indefinitely. It can easily insert corrections, make deletions, and renumber in its memory. Finally, it can type out perfect master copy, when required. This copy will be in uncoded English, as required for the use of the test conductor and his test team.

3.1.5.3   LIBRARY INDEXING AND CODING

Another modern use for computers is in indexing books and reports for library files and catalogs. In this technique, the computer receives the report accession number and abstract, or perhaps the title and table of contents, and makes a word count of typical descriptive words, word combinations, and nomenclature (leaving

Characteristics of Language   39

out inconsequential words such as *a, an, the,* etc.). Then it assigns a set of five or ten of these most prominent *descriptors* to the document (for instance *nose cone, model A-11, reentry, ablation, hypersonic,* and *boundary layer*). This is known as coordinate, or descriptor, indexing.

When the computer has developed its descriptor set, it is ready to type out five or ten *subject* cards listing the report. Complete library indexes, however, are usually presented not on cards but in complete catalogs listing the reports separately under each of their descriptors, perhaps in the order of their accession numbers. The computer can also type new accession lists periodically or revise the catalog at longer intervals.

The scientist who wishes to find a report may look for it listed in the catalog under any of its descriptor headings, or he may perhaps find it under a separate author or source listing which the computer can also prepare. Library research and reference techniques of this sort are discussed at more length in Chapter 13. It can be concluded here, however, that the computer is a powerful ally of the researcher in the task of information retrieval. Such aid is mandatory if everyone is not to be swamped in the stagnating, unread literature of our technical society.

The nature of language is being constantly illuminated by studies conducted with computers. Still, the ultimate questions of language remain. How does a word carry its powerful human responses? How can a simple sentence model complex phenomena with such remarkable ease? What are the basic classifications of grammar? The information available from mathematics and communications theory has been discussed. Another area of language research remains to be examined. This is the area of linguistic and cultural research.

3.2   DEVELOPMENT OF LANGUAGE

3.2.1   Language Sources

The development in prehistory of handtools and pottery can be examined, because these objects remain. Spoken words vanish, sad to say, never to be studied. Thus the manner in which primitive languages developed can only be guessed at or studied in some fashion in the mouths of present-day tribesmen. The spoken languages of all present-day tribes, however, are relatively advanced and cannot be thought of as first attempts at language in any sense. Changes in language, it is true, can be traced in ancient and modern writing, but even these changes do not provide source information. True speech was in use hundreds of thousands of years ago, long before writing appeared, and it is this very ancient age from which data would be most useful.

Guessing at language origins is easy, but not very fruitful. We can, for instance, imagine a caveman sitting on a rock in front of a cave on a sunny morning, viewing a noisy dog. When an idle neighbor appears, we can imagine him pointing to the dog and saying "Wow-wow," as a baby might. Thus the dog becomes *wow-wow*, this tag presumably including the whole complex of dog, dog noises, and dog jumping. Surely, later Neanderthal analysis (several thousand years later) must have separated the *wow-wow* complex into separate items, as dog, dog noise, and dog jumping. A later statement might be "Barking dog jumps." Thus the verb and adjective have been invented, in addition to the original noun (or whatever *wow-wow* was). But all this of course is pure, rather foolish conjecture, and settles nothing.

One promising modern line of language analysis stems from examination of the speech of animals, such as the chimpanzee and baboon. It has been shown, for instance, that the speech of man differs from the speech of the chimpanzee in four important respects. The first difference is man's ability to make entirely new statements about the world (the chimpanzee has a list of only stock comments). The second difference is man's ability to discuss remote places and situations (the chimpanzee is all "here and now"). The third difference is man's ability to create new words at pleasure by forming new combinations of the basic vocal sounds (the chimpanzee has for word assignment only his few basic vocal sounds). The last difference (and not such a clear-cut one) is man's ability to shape his young's conscious use of the language (the chimpanzee's word-learning may be all instinctive).

If the manner in which these basic differences arose in prehistory could be determined, the nature of modern languages would be greatly illuminated. But the discovery of such information clearly requires a concentrated attack by all the resources of linguistics, anthropology, zoology, and related sciences.

Language seems to be as native to man as his distinctive hand and brain. It has enormous influence in determining how he thinks and feels about the world in which he exists. It is both a modelling clay for thinking and a balm for the spirit: a rational and an emotional instrument. Whether these two aspects of language can ever be satisfactorily separated remains for the future to determine.

3.2.2   **Contributions of Linguistics**

The changes which language undergoes as it develops have been studied for centuries by scholars of linguistics. Linguistics is the science of languages. It includes the study of their history and their interrelations (philology). It includes the reconstruction of dead languages and the study of speech sounds (phonology). It includes the study of meaning as related to syllables, words, and word groups (semantics), the study of word variation within a sentence (inflection), and the study of rules for word-group formation (syntax). It also includes the study of human verbal behavior generally, as evidenced in speech and literature.

This enormous field has produced many distinguished scholars whose contributions should be of interest to all writers. Only one result of linguistics study will be discussed further in this subsection, but the student should understand that much of this chapter, and much of this entire textbook, deals with linguistics.

Many languages show resemblances which are so extensive that they cannot be assigned to chance. The reasonable explanation generally is that the languages are descended from a common ancestor and that each developed separately after certain tribal groups separated. Comparative linguistics often makes it possible to reconstruct the initial language in remarkable detail.

One example relates to the English, Dutch, German, Norwegian, Swedish, and Danish languages. These, by linguistics analysis, have been shown to have a common ancestor. This ancestral language, proto-German, has been re-created in surprising detail. Scholars now need only to recover a proto-German manuscript or inscription to confirm their analysis; but so far this material evidence has escaped their search.

Proto-German was not found to be a primitive language. Linguists have been able to show that it is fully as complex and rich in structure as the speech of the most learned scientists. No infant languages are known to exist, as remarked before, except perhaps in the mouths of animals.

3.2.3 Symbolic Writing

Primitive writing was at first symbolic rather than phonetic; that is, some picture or symbol (not a group of letters) was selected to represent the whole word. The picture of a dog, for instance, could be chosen to represent the word *dog*. This system required as many different symbols as there were words in the primitive language—perhaps several hundred. Such a multiplicity of symbols, of course, made reading and writing the language very difficult.

The invention of various forms of symbolic writing took place in several parts of the primitive world. The Egyptian hieroglyphics and the Aztec and Mayan characters are well-known examples. Chinese writing is a modern survival of ancient symbolic writing. The Chinese characters represent complete words, with a different character for every word in the Chinese language. Only scholars are able to learn the hundreds of symbols of the literary portion of the language. There is one other important consequence: Chinese word pronunciations are not fixed by recorded phonetic spellings. Different dialects flourish unchecked in China, even though books may be widespread. Common men from different geographic areas often cannot converse at all, and scholars in this situation may be able to converse only by writing.

3.2.4 Phonetic Writing

Modern English requires the learning of only the 26 letters of the alphabet, combinations of which can represent all the approximately 500,000 words in a large dictionary. Writing in which words are denoted by combinations of the letters of an alphabet is phonetic. The simplicity of this writing results from the fact that the letters stand not for ideas or objects but simply for the

Characteristics of Language

separate sounds which go to make up the spoken word. Thus the word as it appears on paper is a set of instructions telling how the spoken word is pronounced. Phonetic writing then involves three things: the idea or object (called the *referent*), the sound of the word as it is pronounced, and the manner in which the word is recorded on paper.

Pronunciation of a word is relatively fixed in phonetic representation. Phonetic writing in its greatest refinement requires only as many symbols as there are distinct sounds (or phonemes) which the human voice uses in speaking the language. This number varies from language to language. In English there are twenty-four recognized consonants and twelve simple vowels. That all these phonemes can be represented by the 26 letters of the English alphabet is a consequence of the fact that one letter sometimes represents different sounds, as the *a* in *father* and in *fat*.

The fact that the several hundred thousand words of modern English can be represented by combination of 26 letters of the alphabet is of profound social significance. In ancient times, the difficult practice of "picture" writing was left in the hands of priests and learned men, who tended to make a secret of their craft. Thus the records of the past—of history, religion, medicine, astrology, and the like—could be interpreted only by the priestly societies. This fact gave them immense power. They alone were able to prescribe medicine, for instance, or predict the coming of seasonal storms and floods, or forecast the best times for planting, or give directions for travel. In modern societies, on the other hand, because of the ease of reading and writing, the scientific, artistic, and social records are open to the study of everyone.

How alphabetic writing actually came to be invented is not entirely clear. This invention is thought to have occurred only once in history, so difficult and complex was the idea for the untutored mind to grasp. All alphabets the world over are thought, as a consequence, to be derived from an original one which came from the Semitic people of the Sinai Peninsula in the period from 1500 to 1000 B.C. This invention may have been even more significant in shaping the course of history than the invention of decimal notation by Arabian mathematicians, with which it is comparable.

3.3.1   **Words and Definition**

The history of language can lend insight on the problem of word definition. What does an individual word signify to the person who uses it, and how can this meaning best be fixed by definition? The word is the atom of meaning. A smaller division, such as a syllable or letter, carries no meaning with it, only a command for making a meaningless noise. (It is true that a prefix or suffix alone, such as *pre-* or *-able*, can carry meaning of some sort, but these special forms will not be considered here.) Another problem in defining words is the fact that one word can have different meanings (the word *saw*, for instance, has various noun and verb meanings). The answer to this problem is that one does not define the meaning of a word, but of a term, which is one specialized meaning of a word. Thus *terminology* is the specialized set of meanings which attaches to the words used in the practice of a science or art.

How then are all the separate human experiences with regard to a term such as *leg* (where the limb of an animal is meant) to be contained in one short definition? The older, or classical, answer to this problem is to include in the definition of a term only those associations with its referent which everyone can agree on. This makes for such very general and formalized statements of definition as "The leg is that limb of an animal which supports the body." Any more controversial or specialized aspect of a term must be discarded. The usual definition of a term can, in fact, be represented by a simple formula in which the term is first classified, or made a member of a group of similar terms. Following this, such differences from other members of the group are listed as will define the term uniquely. The formula is

$$T = C + d_1 + d_2 + \cdots + d_n$$

where the letters stand successively for *term*, *class*, and *difference*. In the definition of *leg*, a leg is classified as a limb, and then specified as the limb of an animal (not of a tree) which supports the body (not free, as an arm).

A term should be defined, if possible, by words which are simpler than the term. Samuel Johnson violated this rule when he defined a network as "anything reticulated or decussated, at equal distances, with interstices between the intersections."

The important process of classification requires further discussion. What logical process do we follow when we say that a leg is a limb, or that a robin is a bird? We first agree to at least one classifying property of all birds; for instance, that all birds, and only birds, have wings or that all birds, and only birds, have feathers. Then we determine that this property applies in particular to the robin. This classifies the robin as a bird.

The process of classification is extremely important in the study of words. All adjectives, for instance, are the result of such a process occurring in the mind. The adjective *yellow*, for instance, has no independent existence. It is simply that property which is common to all yellow objects, such as yellow bananas, yellow flowers, and yellow dresses. Even the abstract nouns are the result of a mind busy at classification. Truth, for instance, is that property shared by all the correct statements we know. Thus abstract words generally are classifying properties.

Strict observance of the classical rule for definition of objects means that a word cannot be defined simply by giving a synonym for it, nor by describing its properties. The word must first be placed in the smallest possible class of things which will contain it. Do not classify a triangle as a many-sided figure, but rather as a three-sided figure. Another rule is that a term should not be defined by any repetition of itself or of its root. Thus, do not say that a dog is "a dog-like mammal." An exception to this rule allows a compound or built-up term to be defined by repetition of a known part of the compound. Thus it is proper to define a heliport as "a landing place for helicopters."

3.3.2   Extended Definition

The need for understanding definition is important, because many technical and scientific articles have the form of a definition. An article on the laser, for instance, might classify it as a coherent radiation source, comparable to a radar transmitter, and then discuss the differences from radar which make the laser unique. This type of article is called an *extended definition*.

An example of an extended definition will be taken from *The New Yorker*. The quotation is from the introduction to an article entitled "Burglary."

> Since burglary is the most common serious crime locally as well as nationally, it might be supposed that everybody would know precisely what it is; on the contrary, people nearly always mistake it for something else. Not long ago, an elderly lady returned from an evening's outing to her apartment in Manhattan and found her jewelry box empty. She telephoned the police at once and said, "I've been robbed. While I was out, somebody broke into my apartment and ——" "That ain't a robbery, lady," the desk sergeant interrupted her wearily. "That's a burglary." Even the *News*, which has a reputation for being more knowledgeable about crime than elderly ladies are, uses "robbery" and "burglary" interchangeably almost every day. If burglary should not be confused with robbery, it should not be confused with larceny, either. The Penal Law of the State of New York defines robbery as "the unlawful taking of personal property from the person or in the presence of another, against his will, by means of force or violence," and goes on to mention the victim's "fear of injury, immediate or future . . ." A stickup is a robbery. Without force or fear—the elements essential to the crime of robbery—the unlawful taking of someone else's property is larceny. Picking a pocket is larceny. As for burglary, there are three degrees of it in New York State, the third degree being the least serious and the most common. "Burglarly Three," as it is known in the trade, is defined in the Penal Law as the breaking and entering of a building "with intent to commit a crime therein."*

3.3.3 Modern Definition

The science of semantics (the systematic study of meaning in language) holds that the dictionary definition of a word is to a large extent meaningless, or useless. No word can be usefully defined except in the context in which it is actually used, or in its association with other words of the sentence.

It is another principle of semantics that the meaning of a word is subject to change as the environment or conditions of its use are changed. This principle can be forcefully illustrated by the different meanings of the term *democracy* as it is used in the United States, Angola, Communist China, and Russia. All these coun-

*Reprinted by permission from the article "Burglary" by Susan Black; © 1963 The New Yorker Magazine, Inc.

tries are democracies by their own definition. It does not solve the manifest contradiction to say that people other than Americans use the term incorrectly. Word-meaning is determined by usage, not by theory, and on this basis the Chinese, having the most votes, possibly are correct. We can conclude only that meanings are ephemeral and that they change with time and geography.

It may be useful for the engineering student to think of most words as catalogs or arrays of all those properties which a person associates with the word's referent object or action. Mathematical matrices are a means of cataloging the properties of many physical systems. A matrix can catalog the complex state of a vibrating atom, for instance, or the entire set of motion-components of a spacecraft, or the stress-components of a girder. Furthermore, matrices are subject to operational manipulation in the way that words and mathematical symbols are. This array of mental information—the word—can be coded in the human memory perhaps in the same way that a digital computer carries a matrix in its memory. The human nerve cells (neurons) have often been compared to the on-off elements of a computer (diodes and magnetic memory cells).

The idea of the brain cells as two-state, or on-off, elements suggests also that human language, like digital machine language, is fundamentally binary in structure; that is, that grammatical groupings and divisions have a two-part nature rather than, say, a three-part nature. This binary tendency of grammatical divisions has been pointed out by many grammarians (subject and predicate, for instance, noun and verb, adjective and adverb, and preposition and conjunction). The possible utility of such binary groupings lies in the economy of their coding into the brain's speech centers. Examples of this sort of binary codification are given in the structural trees of Appendix B.

It is probably true, in summary, that the real meaning of words lies exactly in the brain's neural patterns. The great jurist Oliver Wendell Holmes, Jr., suggested this when he wrote "A word is not a crystal, transparent and unchanged, it is the skin of a living thought and may vary greatly in color and content according to the circumstances and the time in which it is used."

Word Classes

Three conventional modes of word classification are (1) parts of speech, (2) functional classes, and (3) inflectional classes.

The parts of speech are usually learned in junior high school, together with the school songs and yells. They include nouns, pronouns, adjectives, adverbs, verbs, prepositions, conjunctions, and interjections. A structural tree relating all word classes is shown in Appendix B. The tree is binary in nature; that is, all the elements are paired. The interjection (not used in technical writing) does not appear. On the other hand, the verb is divided into two parts of speech ("motion" verbs and linking verbs) to aid in classifying the basic sentence forms.

Functional classes also appear on the tree. These four classes are (1) substantives (nouns and pronouns), (2) modifiers (adjectives and adverbs), (3) verbs (motion verbs and linking verbs), and (4) connectives (prepositions and conjunctions).

The third classification system includes inflected and noninflected words. Generally speaking, the connectives are noninflected (do not change to show form of usage). All other parts of speech have inflected forms. The nouns, for instance, might add *s* for the plural or *'s* to show possession. The pronouns alter in other ways, as *he, him, her, we,* etc. The verbs, of course, change in many ways (*write, wrote, written,* etc.). The adjectives and most adverbs change to show degree of comparison (*good, better, best,* and *fast, faster, fastest*). Further information on inflection appears in Appendix A.

3.3.5 **Word Group Classes**

There are four types of language structural elements: words, phrases, clauses, and sentences (the paragraph not being a fixed or analytical form). Sentence types are classified and discussed in the appendixes. The basic sentence types of the indicative mode are (1) transitive (active and passive), (2) intransitive, (3) classifying, and (4) attributive. The types of clauses are (1) independent, and (2) dependent. The types of phrases are (1) prepositional, (2) verbal, (3) appositive, and (4) verb.

Although Appendix B does not show all the bewildering varieties of English grammatical forms, the structural trees do have two valid uses. They define the important forms in an explicit, quickly grasped array for the technical student. They also foreshadow the binary language codification which may become important in programming digital computers for language processing.

Choice of Person and Tense

In Chapter 2 a good style in scientific and technical writing was defined as one characterized by a triad of qualities: *clarity, brevity, and variety.* Writing practices which can enhance this sacred triad may be usefully compared with certain composing practices. The composer, before he begins work, must decide which key, which clef, which expression, which time he is going to use. What are the elements of writing which correspond to key, clef, time, and expression? Some of them are *person, tense, voice,* and *mode.* Many beginning writers do not realize that they have these choices to make, and so choose anew and inconsistently in every paragraph. Thus they end by making their style a hopeless muddle. The practiced writer begins action with a staff, clef, and key already arranged on his page, so to speak.

4.1 CHOICE OF PERSON

Choice of person in scientific and technical writing is essentially a choice among personal pronouns. Which of them (*I, we, you, it,* etc.) are permissible to use? Some choice of this sort usually cannot be avoided. People play a central role in scientific activity and the writer must either introduce them explicitly or pretend they don't exist. If he pretends they don't exist, then he has the problem of concealing them in the washroom whenever he is showing guests about the laboratory.

The scientific writer often claims the first prerogative—that of meeting the reader. He uses *I*, *we*, and *you* in his text in ways that will be discussed later. The technical writer, on the other hand, seems forced by convention to pretend that people do not exist. And the circumlocutions he must employ to keep up this subterfuge rob his writing of directness, force, and simplicity.

4.1.1   Use of *It*

It can be a useful word to the scientific and technical writer when there exists a clear and immediate referent (and antecedent) such as *computer* or *knurled knob*. This can be described as specific usage of *it*. But when there exists no clear referent (non-specific usage), *it* stands usually for darkness and confusion. In this squalid role *it* invites into a writer's style such errors as unclear reference, passive construction, and long sentences.

This is a strong indictment against such a small word and must be supported by the evidence. Examples of *it* or *its* used in both the good and bad senses are presented in a passage, from *Aviation Week & Space Technology*, which discusses the importance of the Air Force mission to put a manned laboratory in orbit.

> The Soviet Union entered a new phase of its[1] manned space flight program with its[2] double Vostok flights aimed at perfecting rendezvous and docking techniques. The official Red Army newspaper Red Star noted recently that all of the veteran cosmonauts are now in a special period of intensive training for new types of space flights. Whether these will be more of the rendezvous maneuvers or the orbiting of several people in a larger spacecraft remains to be seen. But it[3] is certain that despite various fluctuations in Western analysis of the Soviet program, it[4] is proceeding consistently to extend man's capabilities in space to the maximum utility.
>
> The Air Force has been given a golden opportunity—perhaps its[5] only chance—to show what man can do in space for military missions. It[6] behooves them to devote their best talents and energy to making this one of the most successful technical development programs in history, similar to the supersonic "X series" research aircraft, the ICBM program and Project Mercury. For on its[7] unqualified success depends the future of military man in space.*

*Reprinted by permission of *Aviation Week & Space Technology*.

In this passage there are seven numbered uses of the pronoun *it* (or *its*). These will be examined in order. The first two uses are clear and worth while. They refer obviously to the Soviet Union (the subject of the sentence).

The third use of *it* ventures on risky ground. Here the reference is to nothing at all definite (nonspecific usage). *It is certain* is a conventional beginning—seemingly innocent. But notice the trouble which this creates further down the line. *It* (No. 4) occurs in the same sentence, referring explicitly to the Soviet program. Thus the same reference pronoun is used in two different senses in the same sentence. The reader's momentary confusion is genuine. He must make a transference of reference. This he does grudgingly, because the original, nonspecific *it* was the subject of the sentence and difficult to disregard.

A restatement of the offending sentence which avoids the difficulties of *it* (No. 3) and *it* (No. 4) might be as follows:

> But despite various fluctuations in Western analysis of the Soviet program, this program is certainly proceeding consistently to extend man's capabilities in space to the maximum utility.

Confusion of another sort occurs a little further along. *Its* (No. 5) obviously refers to *Air Force*, and this reference is in the singular (that is, the collective noun *Air Force* is here chosen as a singular word). So far so good. In the next line *it* (No. 6) occurs again in the phrase *It behooves*. This is a general, or nonspecific, use of *it*, and once again signals trouble down the line. In order to avoid the obviously awkward continuation *It behooves it* (meaning *the Air Force*), the writer continues "It behooves them. . . ." This shifting, however, makes *Air Force* singular in one sentence and plural in the next. Such an error in agreement is usually accepted by the reader, who labels it as trivial. An IBM 7090 computer doing a translation would be outraged by such confusion; but people are nicer than computers. (Of course, any writing which is subject to such rigid deadlines as newswriting can often be criticized in this manner by the careful grammarian and, certainly, by the writer himself when he can study his text at leisure.)

If we accept the convention that *Air Force* is singular, then the

Choice of Person and Tense 53

second paragraph of the quotation can be rewritten in the following manner to avoid trouble with *it*:

> The Air Force has been given a golden opportunity—perhaps its only chance—to show what man can do in space for military missions. The Air Force should devote its best talents and energy to making this one of the most successful technical development programs in history, similar to the supersonic "X series" research aircraft, the ICBM program, and Project Mercury. For on the unqualified success of the manned orbiting laboratory program depends the future of military man in space.

As rewritten here, *Air Force* appears as a singular noun, and all its plural pronoun forms (such as *their*, *them*) have been made singular. In addition, the vague reference of *its* (No. 7) has been made explicit by insertion of the antecedent phrase (*manned orbiting laboratory program*).

In summary, then, the reader is warned to beware of using *it* as his choice of subject. The nonspecific use of *it* is always dangerous, even for a practiced writer. Such usage usually introduces more problems than it solves. Even the specific use of *it*, when standing for such words as *computer*, *diode*, and *radar*, must be attended with care.

The following cautionary rules may prove useful:

1. Beware of using *it* in a nonspecific sense, such as "*It* is certain that. . . ."

2. For specific uses of *it*, there should always exist a specific antecedent (a prior noun to which *it* refers). An example of correct usage is "You program the *computer* by instructing *it* with a tape." Here, *computer* is the antecedent.

3. The antecedent should be the subject of the sentence, a complement, or the noun immediately preceding *it* (unless the relation can be clearly established in some other way, such as by gender).

4. One pronoun should not be used in different senses in any single sentence (as *it* No. 3 and *it* No. 4 were used, for example).

An additional reason for avoiding the nonspecific use of *it* is that such constructions usually invite long sentences and the passive voice. These matters will be discussed at more length later in this chapter (see 4.1.4).

4.1.2   Use of *You*

If the pronoun *it* is the villain of writing, the pronoun *you* can be described as the neglected but faithful country friend of the writer. *You* as a subject or agent in scientific and technical writing is as old as writing itself. Refer to the first example of technical writing quoted in Chapter 1 (1.1.1). This example dealt with an ancient treatment for a broken nose. It can be rewritten for illustration somewhat as follows:

> You should first clean the nose of the patient with two plugs of linen. Then you should place two other plugs of linen saturated with grease inside the two nostrils. You should keep the patient down until the swelling is drawn out, meanwhile applying stiff rolls of linen to hold the nose in place. Repeat these applications of linen each day until the patient recovers.

There are several useful ideas connected with this ancient use of the pronoun *you*. The whole passage gives the effect of simple sturdiness. Such an effect is always obtainable when *you* is used as a subject, because *you* goes naturally with the active voice and with the short, direct sentences of the imperative mode, the simplest form of English sentence construction. The imperative mode and *you* are most suitable for giving commands, instructions, and suggestions. Fortunately, these functions occur often in technical writing.

You can also be employed in a general sense, apart from instructions and suggestions. The great English scientist T. H. Huxley was fond of this usage; in the lecture quoted in Chapter 1 (see 1.2.4), he stated "If the sea were drained off, you might drive a wagon all the way from Valentia. . . ." Rather than being sturdy, this passage is characterized by a rather poetic feeling. (Note also the use of the poetic subjunctive mode. This appears in the verb form *were* following the singular noun *sea*.) Another famous passage of Huxley's, dealing with induction, deduction, and little green apples and employing *you* even more effectively, can be found in Chapter 7 (see 7.2.2).

Choice of Person and Tense   55

The question might well be asked: If *you* is so useful as a subject, why is it not used more? Why do modern technical writers, for instance, prefer the treacherous *it* to the sturdy *you* and the comfortable *we* (to be discussed in the next subsection)? The answer is not clear. At the worst, it may be because modern writers are naturally pompous, and prefer the pompous style which *it* requires. At the best, it may be argued that modern writers are more self-conscious, more aware of a real anonymity, and, falsely, modestly forebear to assert their personalities.

A final comment must be made about the use of *you*. This has to do with the fact that, in the passages just cited, *you* can usually be replaced by the indefinite pronoun *one*. Many writers use *one* sparingly in this manner. There are probably two reasons for this sparing use. *One* is not as flexible as *you*, *one* being suitable as the subject of examples and suggestions but working in poorly with direct commands and the imperative mode. A second reason is that *one* invariably seems more stilted than *you*. Americans regard the extended use of *one* as an English mannerism; possibly the English regard our employment of *one* in this way as a peculiar Yankee habit.

4.1.3   Use of We and I

The pronoun *we* is used more in scientific writing than it is in technical writing. Its use makes for intimacy and directness, reproducing as it does the feeling of a school classroom or a discussion group. Many successful textbooks, in fact, make extended use of *we* to good effect. There exists also the editorial *we* of the newspapers, the royal *we* of reigning monarchs, and the *we* of the college physics teacher who looks at the ceiling, pulls his ear, and asks his class something to this effect: "If we take a 6-volt battery, hook it up with a switch through this coil, then cut in a capacitor here, what do we get if we close the switch?"

The pedagogical, or conjectural, *we* is employed by many eminent scientists to good effect, because it allows for direct theorizing in speech and in print. The following passage shows this conjectural *we* used in an important paper on communications satellites by J. R. Pierce and R. Kompfner. They begin by analyzing conventional communications networks.   (The italics are mine.)

The time will certainly come when *we* shall need a great increase in transoceanic electronic communications.   For example, the United States and Western Europe have a wide community of interests and are bound to demand more and more communication facilities across the Atlantic.   If *we* are to be ready to fill these growing needs, *we* shall have to investigate all promising possibilities.

In doing so, *we* shall certainly want to keep in mind a rule founded on experience.   This rule is that telephone circuits become cheaper the more of them *we* can handle in one bundle.   Then, too, there is the possibility of requirements for television.   In either case, there is a premium on availability of wide bands of frequency.

The submarine cable art is presently distinctly limited in bandwidth.   No doubt its capability in this respect will improve as the years go by, but *we* may well run into economic or technical restrictions not suffered by other techniques.

A chain of UHF scatter links over a northern route might provide channels across the Atlantic Ocean but the quality is dubious, the available bandwidth is limited, and the cost is great.   Indeed, *we* cannot now imagine how *one* might improve quality of bandwidth while at the same time reducing the costs of such a system.   Moreover, such links would not serve for some transoceanic routes.*

Notice in the above passage that Pierce uses *we* consistently as a vehicle for stating his conjectures.   There is one exception to this: the use of *one* in the next to the last sentence to avoid a repetition of the *we* used five words earlier.

The consistent use of *I* in scientific and technical writing is not often observed.   *I*, the most personal of words, is best suited for employment in informal letters, in notes, and in trip reports where a personal opinion is valid.   *I* is also appropriate for the recording of historical actions in which the writer was personally engaged. Very few people make scientific history, however, and there is not much opportunity for this practice.   Dr. Spock injects an occasional *I* in his book on baby care, as do some of the other eminent men who have been quoted.   However, the writer who uses *I* must speak with more authority than the usual technical writer, who may find himself colored blue by his supervisor's blue pencil if he takes this liberty.

*By permission from John R. Pierce and R. Kompfner, "Transoceanic Communication by Means of Satellites," *Proceedings of the IRE*, March, 1959, p. 372.

Impersonal Usage and Passive Voice

There are many ways in which scientific and technical writers avoid the use of personal pronouns. However, all of them require artificial conventions and circumlocutions which are apt to lead the unskilled writer astray. One method is the introduction of a formal cast of characters. These are characters such as *the reader, the author, the engineer,* and *the technician,* all of whom engage in a sort of formal minuet of questions, answers, observations, instructions, and deductions. This method sounds stilted if used extensively. It is not widely employed, compared with impersonal constructions requiring the use of the passive voice.

Use of the passive voice is, for better or for worse, the standard device of most scientific and technical writers who wish to avoid personal pronouns. (*It,* used in the nonspecific sense, will not be counted here as a personal pronoun.) The passive sentence is an indirect and weak construction, open to several types of error. Because it is wordy it invites long sentences, and because of long sentences it invites errors in number and reference. Because it places important elements of the sentence in a subordinate position, it invites obscurity, and because it invites obscurity it invites dangling modifiers. Finally, it inverts the normal time sequence of physical actions, and thus "sicklied over by the pale cast of thought, loses the native hue of resolution."

We can illustrate these weak tendencies in the passive voice rather easily. Take the Neanderthal sentence *Dog bites man* and observe its symmetry, economy, and beauty. The mind accepts this complex structure with relish and appreciation. Now put the sentence in the passive: *Man is bitten by dog.* Notice that two additional, essentially meaningless words have been added. Also notice that the one active agent, *dog,* appears in a minor modifying phrase. This sentence structure does not parallel that of the act itself, which is a simple time sequence of motions culminating in a bloody ankle.

4.1.5   Examples of Passive Construction

An example, from a letter of transmittal, of what might be called the "passive mentality" in sentence construction is quoted next.

Note the typical inverted sentence structure and the placing of important sentence elements in subordinate parts of the sentence. This confusion results from the passive verb phrases which are indicated.

> The intention of this letter *has been determined* as outlining all the requirements necessary before flight test reports *can be written.*
>
> By giving clear examples of the different reports that are necessary, to the flight test team and to the base report team, confusion *will be avoided* surrounding the documentation of these reports and the two teams *can be instructed* in the material each will supply.
>
> The reporting requirements *have been set up* as follows:
>
> 1. Initial telephone report
> 2. Teletype dispatch
> 3. . . . (etc.)

The confused structure of the quoted passage can be clarified if the sentence forms are reconstructed in the active voice.

> This letter *outlines* the requirements necessary for the writing of flight test reports by both the flight test team and the base report team. In addition, it *gives* clear examples of all report types. Study of these examples *can instruct* members of the two teams in the type of material each *will supply*, thus avoiding confusion.
>
> The different report types *are*:
>
> 1. Initial telephone report.
> 2. Teletype dispatch.
> 3. . . . (etc.)

When a modifier is added, the weak tendencies of the passive are generally compounded. *Barking dog bites man,* for instance, might well become, in the passive, *While barking, man is bitten by dog.* Or it might become *While barking, a man is bitten.* This last glib tendency is easily illustrated by reference to scientific literature. In the following quotation from a scientific paper, exactly this sort of ellipsis has occurred:

> *Approximating* the data of Ref. 7 and the more recent estimates of upper atmosphere temperatures cited by Smythe to select the combination of density and temperature yielding a minimum, the minimum mean free path for electron-electron collisions is approximately 50 meters.

The participle *approximating* which occurs in this quotation is said to be dangling because, though an adjective, it has no noun to modify. ("Who is approximating the data?" we can rightfully ask.) Introduction of the immodest personal pronoun *we* can easily clear the matter up. (This introduction of *we* is often possible in scientific writing, though perhaps not possible so often in technical writing.) The passage, when rewritten correctly, might read as follows:

> If we approximate the upper-atmospheric temperature data cited by Ref. 7 and more recently estimated by Smythe, we can select the combination of density and temperature yielding a minimum mean free path. This minimum mean free path for electron-electron collisions is found to be approximately 50 meters.

It is true that dangling participles are numerous in technical literature. Possibly they serve a useful purpose in easing the terrible pinch of the passive construction, like shoelaces which dangle to ease a pinch on the instep. Dangling participles, errors in reference, and errors in number, too, are probably symptomatic, like the sniffles of a cold. The fundamental virus is the false modesty of pretending that people do not exist in technical situations. The struggle to model increasingly complex physical ideas in the face of this restriction demands more flexibility than conventional grammar can sometimes supply. (See 6.2.4 for further discussion of these typical sentence faults.)

4.1.6   Recommended Usage

The writer usually has some choice among personal pronouns open to him. When he picks among them, he can consider the following recommendations:

1. Use *you* in writing directions and suggestions, intermixed as convenient with the imperative mode. An example is *If you have time, set the safety catch before you turn the switch.*
2. Use *one* occasionally to avoid repetition.
3. Use *we* in writing textbooks and scientific material in which speculation and theorizing are required.
4. Use *I* in very informal writing and in nontechnical communications where personal opinion and observation are valid.
5. Use *it* sparingly (in the nonspecific sense).

6. Use the passive in technical writing where it is mandatory, keeping in mind its natural weaknesses.

A good practice is to pick a personal pronoun early and use it consistently. The reader is invited to join a conversational group by this choice. He should be introduced at once to all who intend to participate, and should expect their presence throughout. In the example which follows, too many pronouns have been used; they pop up erratically like people who interrupt.

> The implication of the Mariner 4 flight to Mars—if *you* conclude that Mars is uniformly cratered as *we* do here—is that Mars is uncomfortably like our moon in many respects. Making this assumption, then, *one* is forced to strip Mars of all the useful planetary paraphernalia *everyone* assigned it in the past. *We* mean canals and surface water, marked weather changes, recent geological activity, a molten core, a significant magnetic field, and trapped radiation belts. The fond scientist who once envisioned canals and free water irrigating a verdant vegetable belt (and he and his supporters may have been in the majority) must now accommodate all his plant forms to the dusty surface of a cinder. This is hardly an easy task, as *you* and *I* can attest.

This passage represents not scientific writing but science writing; that is, writing of primary interest for the layman. However, it displays a bad habit which all writers can fall into: the confusing use of personal pronouns. The "party group" in the passage includes many persons: *you, I one, we,* and *everyone* (not to mention *the fond scientist,* or *he*). All these people speak as erratically as school children.

The passage can be easily amended by the uniform use of *we,* which is an appropriate subject in science writing.

> The implication of the Mariner 4 flight to Mars—if *we* conclude that Mars is uniformly cratered—is that Mars is uncomfortably like our moon in many respects. Making this assumption, then, *we* must strip Mars of all the useful planetary paraphernalia it was assigned in the past; that is, canals and surface water, marked weather changes, recent geological activity, a molten core, a significant magnetic field, and trapped radiation belts. The fond scientist who once envisioned canals and free water irrigating a verdant vegetable belt (and he and his supporters may have been in the majority) must now accommodate all his plant forms on the dusty surface of a cinder. This is hardly an easy task, as *we* can attest.

CHOICE OF TENSE

Rules for Choice

The choice of proper tense in scientific and technical writing fortunately can be guided by simpler rules than can the choice of person. The tenses which are normally available include those of the indicative mode and the one tense of the imperative mode, the present. This in effect gives seven tenses to consider here, the three simple and the three compound (or perfect) tenses of the indicative (with no distinction needed as to active and passive), and the present imperative tense.

After having sorted out the available tenses, we next need to sort out, or classify, the types of scientific and technical writing which have regard to tense. Writing can be classified for this purpose into six categories. These are: (1) present or contingent facts, (2) historical facts and past actions, (3) plans, predictions, and promises, (4) contractual statements and specifications, (5) general truths and definitions, and (6) commands and instructions. (These types may sometimes overlap.)

Each category of information has a recommended tense (or tenses), which can be summarized by the following list:

1. Present or contingent facts—use present tense:

    The booster *is* on the launch pad.

    A numerical calculation *can be made* whenever the loss ratio *is determined*.

2. Historical facts and past actions—use past tense (use perfect tenses if time reference is in the past):

    A linearized analysis *indicated* the presence of disturbing torques.

    The design of the radar *was* not adequate for high-speed search.

    Airplanes *have burned* kerosene since the introduction of the jet engine.

    Airplanes *had burned* gasoline before the introduction of the jet engine.

3. Plans, predictions, and promises—use future tense with *will* (use future perfect tense if time reference is in the future):

62

The launch *will occur* at 0800 at the Pacific Missile Range.

When the representative comes, he *will find* everything in order.

The installation *will have been completed* before the vehicle is shipped.

4. Contractual statements and specifications—use future tense with *shall*:

The range of temperature through which the equipment *shall operate* is −180 to +95°C.

The contractor *shall receive* shipment at his Tulsa plant.

5. General truths and definitions—use present tense:

Hydrogen *is* lighter than air.

The angles of an equilateral triangle *are* all equal.

One horsepower *is* equivalent to 33,000 foot-pounds of work per minute.

Reliability *is increased* by good design.

6. Commands and instructions—use present imperative:

Raise your left elevator.

If the drawer sticks, *wiggle* it back and forth.

Determine the distance of travel by resolving the vectors along their component axes.

4.2.2   Comments on Tense

Most explanatory scientific and technical writing can be accomplished by use of the simple present and past tenses. And generally even the past tense can be avoided if no reference is made to previous work. Plans for the future are best indicated by use of the future tense with the auxiliary verb *will*. *Shall* is understood, from a widespread convention in specification writing, to indicate a contractual obligation to perform. *Shall* should not be lightly used, therefore, when it might be open to misinterpretation.

The simple tenses (present, past, and future) all refer to the present (or now) as principal time origin. A special origin (stated or implied) is understood with perfect tenses. Explanatory examples of these time relations appear below.

SIMPLE TENSES

Present: He works here.   (Action occurs at present
                                     time.)

Past: He worked here.   (Action occurred prior to
                                     present time.)

Future: He will work here.   (Action will occur after
                                     present time.)

PERFECT TENSES

Present: He has worked here   (Action occurred between
            since Easter.   special time origin—Easter—
                                     and present time.)

Past: He had worked here   (Action occurred prior to
            before Easter.   special time origin.)

Future: He will have worked   (Action will occur between
            here before next   present time and special future
            Easter.   time origin.)

The time relations implied by the use of the perfect tenses are understood instinctively by most people, yet they are actually fairly tricky. Problems can be avoided by use of the simple tenses and specific dates. For instance, *The spacecraft will have been at Cape Kennedy nine months before it is launched next April 10* should be replaced by some clearer, more informative statement. A better statement would be *The spacecraft was sent to Cape Kennedy on 3 July. It will probably be launched on 10 April, after being at the Cape nine months.*

4.2.3   Use of Conditional Statements

A special caution is in order regarding the use of certain auxiliary verbs, here called the "conditional" auxiliaries; namely, *could, may, might, ought,* and *should.* All of them have their proper uses, but sometimes they have improper uses too. Improper usage occurs when a writer inserts them specifically to confuse or obscure the meaning of a statement with the intention of showing caution. The following is an example of such usage:

> The analysis *could* be interpreted to justify the initial choice of parameters, but probably *should* not be used in this manner without extreme care. If it *may* be used in this sense for the present, then the initial choice of parameters appears to be justified. Further analysis *might* support this conclusion.

64

The conditional auxiliaries are condemned here not because they exhibit caution but because they exhibit bad writing. Caution is best indicated by other means, such as by direct statement:

This analysis is difficult to interpret. It appears to indicate that the initial choice of parameters is justified. Further analysis is needed to support this conclusion.

5 *Effective Sentences*

5.1 SENTENCE VARIETY

Sentences should vary in their relative complexity in order not to bore the reader with their monotony. This rule is a simple one to follow if the writer keeps his wits about him. Variations in sentence structure and length, use of parenthetical statements, changes from a normal word order, and occasional questions can all enhance the interest of a passage. Examples of these variations are shown in a typical passage of technical literature:

> (1) The objective of the Apollo program is manned exploration of the moon. (2) The program is designed to place the first man on the moon (and return him safely to earth) in 1970. (3) This objective must be accomplished, if possible, within the present state of the art, which means it must be accomplished with a minimum number of now unproven systems and techniques. (4) Among the unproven systems presently required are the fuel cell, the liquid-hydrogen upper boost stages, and the space navigation system. (5) Necessary new techniques include rendezvous, moon landing, and superorbital reentry. (6) The will of the American people to complete the program in the face of its many dangers is not final, but the fact that the program can open the resources of the moon and planets to their perpetual use is clear.

The six sentences of this passage can be characterized roughly as follows, if we attempt to examine their variety:

1. *Simple* sentence—linking verb—twelve words
2. *Simple* sentence—passive verb—twenty words—parenthetical element
3. *Complex* sentence—various verbs—thirty words
4. *Simple* sentence—linking verb—twenty-one words—inverted order
5. *Simple* sentence—active verb—ten words
6. *Compound complex* sentence—various verbs—forty-one words

What is an adequate sentence variety? No formula can be given, but the passage just quoted appears to fulfill this requirement reasonably well. The student should occasionally examine his own sentences in this manner to check their change of pace.

5.2   SENTENCE COMPLEXITY

5.2.1   Measures of Complexity

5.2.1.1   SENTENCE LENGTH

All sentences probably can be reduced in complexity below a certain theoretical level by the use of good writing technique. For this reason, some quick measure of sentence complexity would be useful to determine when a sentence needs reworking. Such a measure could be used by the student writer or by the Armed Forces in their specifications for comprehension level in reports and manuals. The simplest measure is sentence word count, or average number of words per sentence. This number is usually set at twenty when a specification is made. The average length for the passage quoted in the preceding paragraph is twenty-two words, principally because of the great length of the sixth sentence—forty-one words.

5.2.1.2   SENTENCE INDEXES

It is plain that a measure of sentence complexity more sophisticated than word count is desirable. One useful attempt at such a measure is called the *Fog Index*.* Application of this method gives a number hopefully equal to the number of years of school education needed for understanding of the passage in question. A

*Robert Gunning, *The Technique of Clear Writing*, McGraw-Hill Book Company, New York, 1952, pp. 36–37.

Fog Index of 12 associated with some passage means that a high school education suffices for its ready understanding.

The Fog Index (F.I.) is determined by the formula

$$F.I. = 0.4 \, (A + P)$$

where A is the average number of words per sentence (counting independent clauses as separate sentences) in a sample of at least 100 words and P is the polysyllable count (words of three syllables or more) per 100 words. The polysyllable count should exclude all capitalized words, combinations of short words, such as *thereafter*, and any verbs which become polysyllables only as a result of adding an inflectional ending.

The Fog Index works reasonably well for ordinary checks of reading level. However, it is easy to imagine theoretical objections to this Index. Sentences are made up of independent and dependent clauses, of several types of phrases, and of various parenthetical elements, and all these conceivably should be taken into account. Sentence construction with regard to order and symmetry is also highly important. The effects of these elements on sentence complexity will be examined in succeeding paragraphs.

The student should appreciate, at this point, that it is not enough to be against all forms of bad writing in order to write simple, clear sentences. Cancer can be easily condemned in this fashion too. The difficulty does not lie in the condemnation; it lies in the cure. How are we to decide which of our sentences are too difficult, and how can we best rewrite them? The cure for bad writing, like the cure for cancer, must be discovered by thoughtful study.

5.2.2 Sentence Symmetry

Skilled writers often use long sentences to good effect. They do this by constructing their sentences in a symmetrical, or balanced, fashion, matching clause with clause or phrase with phrase so that the resultant sentence structure is very orderly. One such example can be quoted from Lincoln's Second Inaugural Address, in which he discussed the problems of securing a lasting peace after the Civil War.

With malice toward none, with charity for all, with firmness in the right, as God gives us to see the right, let us strive on to finish the work we are in, to bind up the nation's wounds, to care for him who shall have borne the battle, and for his widow and orphan—to do all which may achieve and cherish a just and lasting peace among ourselves, and with all nations.

This one sentence of Lincoln's is seventy-three words in length, and yet it is clear and forceful. How did it attain such clarity and power? The answer may lie in the sentence's beautiful focus and balance. It is what might be called an "aerodynamically clean structure." Its focus and balance are genuine, and can be illustrated as follows:

With malice toward none, with charity for all, with firmness in the right . . .	}	let us strive on	}	to finish the work . . . to bind up the nation's wounds, to care for him . . . to do all . . .

Four dependent clauses used as adjectives have been indicated in the above array by dots. These clauses may seem to throw the structure out of harmonious balance, but it is exactly this minor disproportion which lends interest and variety to the fundamental balance. Without this, Lincoln's noble effect would have been one of sing-song monotony. The passage illustrates both the power and clarity of balanced, or parallel, phrasing and the small embroidery of disproportion which must conceal the larger regularity.

5.2.3   Sentence Memory Level

There exists an additional aspect of sentence complexity which is very difficult to define or measure. This is the aspect which relates to the brain's capability for "flash" comprehension. Sentences, while they are being read, can require that the brain keep in simultaneous memory two, three, four, five, six, or more contingent facts. In the sentence *The fourth diode on the right is faulty*, we have to carry along three words before we get to *is*, when the pattern of the subject suddenly falls into place. These words are *diode, fourth, right*. The mind can accommodate this temporary complexity only to a certain degree.

It is easy to imagine a very difficult short sentence of this nature. An example is *That you go to the fourth house to the left of the ninth house east when you leave here is not certain.* This sentence has a word count of twenty-two, twenty-one of the words being monosyllables. Its difficult nature lies not in vagueness but in the growing burden of associated ideas which the reader must carry along to the verb *is* before they are resolved. The sentence can be rewritten in an easier manner as follows:

> When you leave here, go four houses to the left and nine to the east. But this is not certain.

The words are practically the same in both versions of this passage, but the relative order in which the key elements are introduced has been changed. In addition, a second principal verb has been introduced to "absorb" some of the modifying phrases earlier in the sentence.

This experiment should serve to show that a fundamental measure of sentence complexity is some quantity we might describe as *required memory level*. This is the maximum number of elements we are required to keep in mind at any point in the sentence. Many word puzzles are difficult to solve because of this sort of complexity. One example is the old henhouse puzzler: If a hen and a half lays an egg and a half in a day and a half, how many eggs does one hen lay in one day? The Fog Index of this sentence is eleven, and presumably it can be understood by a high school graduate.

Normal sentence order, discussed next, is set up to reduce the required memory level and also to make clear the relations between various sentence elements.

5.2.4   Sentence Order and Clarity

In general, normal sentence order has been established over centuries of human usage to provide the most efficient framework for human thought patterns. The standard sentence may be compared to the standard axe handle in this. The former fits the human mind most comfortably for communication; the latter fits the human hand grip most comfortably for chopping.

What is normal sentence order? The topic may be examined in many bewildering aspects. The normal order of the principal elements of the declarative sentence is *subject—verb—complement* (where the complement may be a direct object, indirect object, predicate noun, etc.). When the possible modifiers of each element (including words, phrases, and clauses) are considered, the ordering becomes more complicated. This ordering can be diagrammed as follows (leaving off consideration of the complement for the present):

Adjective–Noun–Phrase–Clause | Adverb–Verb–Phrase–Clause

All the modifiers attach to the noun or the verb. In a given sentence some elements may be missing or some may be compounded (there may be several adjectives, for instance), but such deviations do not affect the sequence. Adverbs probably follow the verb they modify as often as they precede it. Those adverbs which modify other adverbs or adjectives are not indicated on the diagram. Such adverbs, of course, normally precede the word they modify, as "*extremely* black hair," or "*very* quickly lost."

One convenient sentence can be written now which illustrates the normal order of sentence modification:

Swift airplanes from Brazil which we never see silently land at the airport after everyone has gone.

The modifying words and word groups of this sample sentence are placed exactly as they appear in the diagram ("airplanes," of course, being the subject noun, and "land" being the verb). It should be interesting to experiment with changing the order of the modifying elements (keeping the subject noun and verb fixed in position). The student who attempts this will find that the order of the subject noun modifiers cannot be altered in any way without awkwardness or damage to the efficiency of the sentence. The verb modifiers, on the other hand, can be moved quite freely about the sentence without marked harm. The following are examples of some possible altered sequences for the verb modifiers:

At the airport after everyone has gone, swift airplanes from Brazil which we never see land silently.

Silently, after everyone has gone, swift airplanes from Brazil which we never see land at the airport.

It appears that a writer has the liberty to depart from the normal order for verb modification whenever he finds it useful. The sequence of noun and noun modifiers, on the other hand, is fairly rigidly fixed. This curious situation probably results from the fact that, in a given sentence, there are usually many more nouns than verbs; and noun modification, to be clear, must be rigidly controlled.

It is lucky that verb modification can be so flexible. Often the verb has a complement associated with it, clamoring for position in competition with the modifiers, and the writer (like a mother with quarreling children) must decide which gets the place of honor.

An example of the traffic jam which can occur west of the verb (at the intersection of complement and modifier) appears in the following sentence, written in seemingly normal word order:

> He inserted the nozzle of the rocket engine from the spacecraft which was damaged in the test chamber.

There are many ways in which this sentence can be read. The confusion results from the fact that some modifiers can attach to *inserted*, some to *nozzle*, some to *engine*, some to *spacecraft*, etc., and normal word order is not adequate to sort all these relations out. The sentence must be rewritten to take better advantage of flexible positioning of the verb modifiers.

> He inserted in the test chamber the damaged nozzle of the rocket engine from the spacecraft.

(This sentence could have been rewritten as two sentences, of course, but the rules of the modification experiment demanded that it remain as one sentence, retaining its subject noun and its verb in unaltered form. This has been done.)

Some additional topics relating to sentence order and clarity include the use of the passive voice, the splitting of clauses, and the use of infinitives. It is in these difficult areas, where simple rules cannot be given, that the experience and judgment of the practiced writer come most notably into play in producing clear, emphatic sentences.

5.2.5   Logical Signposts

Logical signposts in writing include such words as *however, therefore, accordingly, consequently, then, furthermore, moreover, nevertheless, hence,* and *also.* These words, usually called *conjunctive adverbs,* are employed to show the turns in logic which an argument or explanation has taken. They are not needed in defining the structure of the sentence, and so come free to the reader as a sort of bonus from the goodhearted writer. The ungenerous writer, on the other hand, is niggardly of such signposts and offers them rarely, perhaps to let his reader stumble along with the impression that the writing is unusually profound.

Another use of conjunctive adverbs is to connect sentences smoothly and make smooth transitions between paragraphs. Writing which seems jerky or halting often results from inadequate use of the conjunctive adverbs or of certain phrases which serve the same purpose, such as *on the other hand* and *as a result*.

The ordinary conjunctions act as logical signposts also. Rather than employing a monotonous *and* to connect all clauses, the beginning writer should always consider whether *but* or *nor* are not more to the point. The subordinating conjunctions, particularly *if, although, as, since,* and *because*, have a strong role in establishing logical relations, too, and should be used liberally.

5.2.6   Recommendations for Clarity

Recommendations dealing with sentence clarity which should be appropriate for the beginning or unskilled writer are:

1. Vary the structure of succeeding sentences to avoid monotony.
2. Employ some measure of sentence complexity, such as the Fog Index, for an occasional check.
3. Write sentences averaging no more than twenty words in length.
4. Arrange the elements of every sentence in the best order for normal comprehension.
5. Write sentences containing no more than two or three clauses of any sort.
6. Use logical signposts freely.

A useful comment on clarity can be found in Lawrence Sterne's *Tristram Shandy*. In it, the hero, Tristram Shandy, discusses his Uncle Toby, who, it seems, fought with the Duke of Wellington as an artillerist. Uncle Toby is always plaguing Tristram with technical discussions which make his head swim.

[My Uncle Toby] proceeded next to Galileo and Torricellius, wherein, by certain Geometrical rules, infallibly laid down, he found the precise part to be a "Parabola"—or else an "Hyperbola,"—and that the parameter, or "latus rectum," of the conic section of the said path, was to the quantity and amplitude in a direct ratio, as the whole line to the sine of double the angle of incidence, formed by the breech upon an horizontal line;—and that the semiparameter, ——stop, my dear Uncle Toby—stop!

Evidently Uncle Toby did not follow rules for clarity of the type we have recommended.

5.3 PARALLEL STRUCTURE

The ideas of balanced and parallel structure have been illustrated in the preceding subsection with a passage from Lincoln's Second Inaugural Address. The principle of parallelism can be applied at all levels of structure; that is, to ideas, to paragraphs, to sentences, to clauses, to phrases, to individual words, to the headings and subheadings of an outline, to briefing posters, to table entries, to simple lists, and to items of a series. Anywhere coordinate, or equal, ideas are associated in writing, their statement is best made in parallel grammatical form. This principle is very powerful in obtaining clarity. The idea of parallelism also involves the idea of subordination. That is, express parallel ideas in parallel grammatical form, and subordinate ideas in a subordinate or (modifying) form.

5.3.1 Coordinate Constructions

The coordinating conjunctions, such as *and*, *or*, and *but*, all link coordinate ideas. Therefore, for the sake of clarity, constructions joined by these words are best expressed in parallel grammatical form. A detailed paralleling of grammatical elements is not always possible, but the major elements should be, and can be, constructed similarly. Here are examples of faulty and of correct use:

FAULTY: During World War II, solid-propellant rockets were used in bazookas and to fire air-to-air cannons.
CORRECT: During World War II, solid-propellant rockets were fired by bazookas and by air-to-air cannons.

FAULTY: In the electronics industry, skilled technicians are needed to make high-quality solder joints and must excel in welding.
CORRECT: In the electronics industry, skilled technicians are needed to make high-quality solder joints and welds.

74

5.3.2   Lists and Enumerations

In a list or enumeration of any sort (including entries in a table), each member or item should be stated in a parallel grammatical form. Here are examples of faulty and correct parallel listings:

FAULTY	CORRECT (NOUNS)	CORRECT (GERUND PHRASES)
Recreations:	*Recreations:*	*Recreations:*
Playing golf	Golf	Playing golf
Listening to good music	Music	Listening to music
Chess contests	Chess	Playing chess
Learning to ski	Skiing	Skiing
Bridge lessons	Bridge	Playing bridge
The swimming team	Swimming	Swimming
Attending movies	Movies	Attending movies
Basketball and hockey	Basketball Hockey	Playing basketball Playing hockey

The following is an example of faulty parallelism in a briefing poster:

FAULTY: **Flash Report**
- Report will include countdown, flight history, recovery operations, post-recovery, each systems analysis, and what objectives obtained
- Prepared by field-site team
- Transmitted to contractor within 24 hours
- Will be made a part of final report

CORRECT: **Flash Report**
- Must include sections on countdown, flight, recovery, post-recovery analysis, subsystems performance, and attainment of test objectives
- Must be prepared by launch-site team
- Must be transmitted to contractor within 24 hours
- Must be part of final report

5.3.3   Series Construction

Another important application of the principle of parallel structure is in constructing a series of items within a sentence. Not only must the members of the series be stated in a parallel form, but they must all relate in a logical manner to the word or phrase

Effective Sentences   75

which introduces the series. It often happens that, with a long series, the manner in which the first element was introduced is forgotten or obscured by the time the last element is stated. This happens particularly when a preposition, article, relative pronoun, subordinating conjunction, auxiliary verb, or infinitive is the introductory element. In order to make such parallelism clear, it is considered good practice to repeat the introductory element when length or variation of any of the items might tend to obscure the strict parallelism. The following are examples of correct usage:

The pilot *must* check his fuel supply, trim his aircraft, signal the tower, and, after receiving clearance, *must* prepare to land.

The test conductor told him *that* the voltage regulation was unsteady part of the time and *that* he must correct it.

The engineer is encouraged *in* the study of network theory and *in* the practice of wiring and soldering.

The launch pad is occasionally visited *by* distinguished guests who are proponents of space flight and *by* photographers.

It is possible that a series can be a member in itself of a larger series. The nested series requires special care in phrasing and punctuation. In the diagram, note the importance of the repeated elements in making the thought-parallelism clear; note also the use of *and*.

He instructed *those* technicians *who* had come in from our desert base *and who* had come back from the launch complex, *and those* interested engineers from the local area, in the elements of flight-test planning.

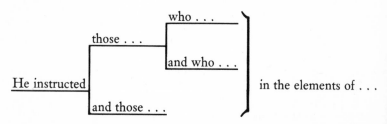

The correlative conjunctions (such as *both...and* and *neither ...nor*) should each be followed by a parallel grammatical element.

FAULTY: The Ranger 6 moon probe had *both* a navigational success *and* resulted in an instrumentation failure.

76

CORRECT: The Ranger 6 moon probe experienced *both* a navigational success *and* an instrumentation failure.

5.4   SUBORDINATE STRUCTURE

Proper subordination means creating proper grammatical relations between the important and unimportant elements of a sentence. Ordinarily, the important elements of a sentence should appear in the verb, in the subject, or in the complement, and the subordinate elements should appear as modifiers. A sentence can fail in three ways: (1) by lacking subordination entirely, (2) by using important elements as modifiers, and (3) by giving trivial elements a position of importance.

5.4.1   Lack of Subordination

The sentences which children write often lack subordination entirely. Their short, jerky sentences seem confused because they have no clear focus or point. The following is a typical example of a child's "technical writing":

> The flashlight has this button. You push it with this finger and a light comes out and you can find things. You can make a scary face. I scared my sister once but when your mother comes in she gets mad. I mean she gets mad and makes you turn it off. When you leave it on I mean. The flashlight helps you find things under the bed. You have to push this button.

There is no subordination at all in this paragraph, no attempt to separate trivial elements from key technical elements by use of modification. It is interesting to observe that this purpose is served by repetition, however. The elements which seem important to the child are simply repeated for emphasis. Using repetition is an elementary method of focusing meaning. Using subordination correctly is a more efficient, more sophisticated method.

5.4.2   Faulty Subordination

A second way in which subordination can be used improperly is in the placing of an important statement in a modifying position. An example of this faulty practice appears in the sentence *Flight to the planets and beyond cannot be accomplished before 1975 with human pilots aboard.* The important part of the sentence,

Effective Sentences   77

"human pilots," is buried at the end. The word *human* is actually a modifier within a modifier. The sentence should be recast with this important idea introduced early and prominently: *Men will not pilot spacecraft to the planets and beyond before 1975.*

5.4.3 Subordination of Details

The third way in which subordination can be used improperly is in failing to place a trivial detail in a trivial position. An example of this fault appears in

> The chamber where the execution was to take place was dark and hushed. You noticed the low hum of a high-voltage power transformer, the sharp smell of ozone, and the dirty walls.

This example, of course, is ludicrous because a trivial detail has been misplaced. A better statement would insert this triviality as a modifier.

> The dark, hushed chamber with its dirty walls seemed full of the smell of ozone as you entered. Then you noticed the low hum of a high-voltage power transformer. In this chamber an execution would take place.

5.5 EMPHASIS

In discussing parallel and subordinate structure, we dealt directly with sentence form. In discussing emphasis we deal more directly with content than with form. There are five ways in which verbal emphasis can be employed to shape the focus and meaning of a sentence. These are (1) emphasis by flat statement, (2) emphasis by position in section or paragraph, (3) emphasis by proportion of whole, (4) emphasis by stylistic treatment, and (5) emphasis by repetition.

5.5.1 Emphasis by Statement

Emphasis by flat statement is a well-known device of advertising and oratory which the scientific and technical writer, particularly the sales brochure writer, should not disregard entirely. Of course he cannot say "This type of optimization analysis is the choice of all discriminating engineers," or "Use of this type of circuit redundancy will insure the perpetuation of our finest traditions of democracy." On the other hand, he can say something as emphatic as "This warning is highly important. Under no circumstances use this equipment with the interlocks inoperative."

In a less strident manner, he can also gain attention by remarks of this sort: "Consider the consequences of this statement with care . . . ," or "This remark is important enough to be repeated . . . ," or "One statement can be made summarizing the whole argument . . . ," or "The tremendous implications of this formula must not be overlooked. . . ."

5.5.2 Emphasis by Position

Scholars of literary style usually argue that the positions of greatest emphasis in a section or paragraph are at the very beginning and end. The positions of least emphasis are in the middle. This conclusion can be supported by consideration of Lincoln's Gettysburg Address. The whole populace remembers the last phrase—"that government of the people, by the people, and for the people shall not perish from the earth." Probably as many people remember the beginning: "Four score and seven years ago, our fathers brought forth on this continent. . . ." But not so many people remember the interior phrases, noble though they may be—". . . the last full measure of devotion." How does the rest of it go?

In comparing an expository style with a literary style, it may be argued that in the former the position of greatest emphasis is clearly at the beginning of the passage. This results because the expository writer often states what he is going to show or prove at the beginning of the passage. Or he often summarizes a description before entering into its details. Many readers look at the opening statement only, especially if they are in a hurry. Thus greatest emphasis can usually be given a statement if it is placed at the beginning of a section or paragraph in scientific and technical writing. This is a consequence of technical reading habits and of the fact that suspense is not a technique for gaining emphasis.

5.5.3 Emphasis by Proportion

Emphasis in all writing can be obtained by sheer weight of words. We are inclined to emphasize the importance of our physical ailments by discussing them volubly with friends. For instance, we might give a long catalog of the consequences of a cold or a sore elbow. This same device can be used in expository writing. We can write extensively about an idea or proposal and make it important. The danger is that our proposal will suffer the same end as our recital of ills. Unless the topic is important enough to justify extended treatment, we end by boring everyone.

5.5.4   Emphasis by Style

Making splashy or colorful statements in scientific and technical writing to create interest or attention is risky. The risk is not that the statement will go unnoticed. It will be noticed, indeed, and it will be condemned. The situation is the same as that of Caesar's wife, who also had to be above suspicion; that is, above the need for making a case by any means other than a sober statement of fact. This stricture applies particularly to such colorful faults in technical writing as the use of slang, exaggeration, random underlining and italicizing, and novelty words.

Some usage of metaphor—figures of speech—is proper, however. Metaphor is defined as the transference of meaning between words and phrases by analogy, or by a comparison which shows some unsuspected likeness. The language of the scientist and engineer would be poorer, indeed, without the use of phrases such as *booster skirt, engine apron, rocket tail, wind sock,* and *belly tank.* The comparisons are conventional now, but at one time they had to be invented by some mind busy at analogical extension of the language from the old to the new.

5.5.5   Emphasis by Repetition; Paragraph Unity

Important material or difficult material is sometimes repeated in the hope that if it didn't "get across" the first time, it might the second time. This sort of repetition is dangerous unless the reader is clearly warned of the fact. Chaucer (see 1.2.1) asked the reader to excuse his repetition when he was trying to explain difficult ideas to his small son. "It seems better to write a good idea down twice in case he forgets it once," he states.

The technical writer is also open to the temptation of repetition. The misuse of repetition can occur when the writer makes one attempt at an explanation and decides he has failed. Under these circumstances he should cross out the failure. Instead, however, many writers add a second explanation, taking a totally new approach. The reader, who must untangle the first brier patch of explanation as best he can, enters on the second explanation without understanding that it is a restatement. A few minutes later he takes an aspirin in despair, thinking he has failed to understand two very important ideas. Thus, it is dangerous to repeat any statement or explanation without making the fact of repetition plain. It is also dangerous to let a bad explanation remain in the hope it might prove useful, like a broken car jack in the trunk of a car. Get a new explanation; get a new jack.

So far we have advised caution in the repetition of ideas. Repetition of certain words, however, should be encouraged, even though the repetition seems inelegant or redundant. An example occurs in the sentence *An attitude-control system controls the attitude of the Tiros satellite.* The repeated words *attitude* and *control* must be accepted because they are difficult to avoid. *Attitude-control* is a standard label for the system in question; it would be confusing to describe this system in any way as not performing this explicit function.

Another useful form of word repetition occurs when certain key words are used like nails to "nail" the sentences of a paragraph together, so to speak. The following passage from a manual uses the key words *time delay*, *latching*, *arming*, and *relay* in this manner. The repetition may seem excessive; it should be understood, however, that explosive circuits are being discussed and explicit statement is mandatory. There must be no possibility of confusion resulting from unclear reference words such as *these* and *it*.

> The launch timer consists of 19 relays (four are latching and eight are time-delay relays). Latching relays K1 and K2 are redundant pyro relays that latch either in the safe or in the armed condition. In the armed condition, voltage is diverted to the sequencer and, by relays K3 and K4, to the separation system. Latching relays K3 and K4 are redundant logic latching relays. In the armed condition, voltage is directed across the abort relays K5 and K6 to energize the separation relays K7 and K8, and to energize the time-delay relays K9 and K10.
> The time-delay relays K9 and K10 . . .

In reading this passage, the student should note how repetition of key words is used not only for absolute clarity of presentation but also to link sentence to sentence and paragraph to paragraph. This linking of ideas is an important element of paragraph coherence. The problem of writing smoothly, so often a matter of despair for beginning writers, can sometimes be solved by conscious use of the sort of repetition they seek to avoid.

6 *Sentence Criticism*

The principles of effective sentence construction were presented in Chapter 5. In this chapter, criticism of actual sentence-writing practices will be presented, and typical ineffective and faulty sentences will be classified, discussed, and rewritten.

6.1 WORDY SENTENCES

6.1.1 Writing With Phrases

All writers are subject to a lazy tendency to substitute ready-made phrases for their own home-made phrases. This practice can be compared to selecting stock telegrams from Western Union's catalog of ready-made greetings when you wish to send a birthday message to your mother-in-law. The trouble with this practice is that stock phrases are very coarse information units; their use allows little subtlety, flexibility, or economy of information transmission. The Western-Union sort of phrases which are common in scientific and technical writing include *It is probably well known that . . . , One of the most important items that . . . , As has already been described . . . , When one considers the above phenomena in the light of present knowledge . . . , It is a basic and fundamental principle that. . . .* Most of these phrases are opening statements which actually may serve a need other than that the writer intends: They allow the lazy writer to get his thoughts in gear while he attempts to think of something worth while. Unfortunately such writers are kept so busy scribbling out these long phrases that they never engage their higher brain centers. The result is gobbledygook—writing with a large word content and a small thought content. The great need in writing, of course, is for a large thought content and a small word content—more explanation and fewer words.

The writer should make it a point to think of words, not phrases, when he is searching for a means to express himself. He should not, like a bird building a nest, pick up all the stringy clauses and flashy phrases which he chances to find in the neighborhood. The practice of speedreading has probably been developed as a means of countering this sort of bad writing. Its proponents suggest implicitly that much of business and technical writing is wordy and coarse, and that whole phrases and clauses require no more of the reader's notice than a single word should. This state of affairs—the reader fights back—would probably not exist if the writer did his duty and wrote as he should write—word by word. A quotation from George Orwell can reinforce this statement:

> Prose [these days] consists less and less of words chosen for the sake of their meaning, and more and more of phrases tacked together like the sections of a prefabricated henhouse. . . . Modern writing at its worst . . . consists in gumming together long strips of words which have already been set in order by someone else.

6.1.2 Redundancy

Redundancy must not be confused with repetition. Repetition often serves a useful purpose (see 5.5.5). Redundancy, on the other hand, is here defined as the needless repetition or restatement of any word or idea. This should not be compared with redundancy in physical design to insure reliability (placing two valves in parallel, for instance, to insure that at least one will turn on when a signal is applied). Writing constitutes a series network, and redundancy in such a loop is usually wasteful. There are many ways in which a writer can repeat himself unknowingly. The following are sample phrases in which this occurs:

Today's modern digital-analog computer design is . . .

84

Here in this section you will find . . .
Approximately six or eight men can do the job . . .
What *systems* and *equipment* are needed . . .
The *resultant effect* is to . . .
Any *unnecessary* parts *will not be needed* . . .
Replace the books on the shelves *again* . . .
Deflate the tire by *letting out the air* . . .

Needlessly defining a word or operation constitutes a special form of redundancy. An example of this is *Measure the input resistance by determining the number of ohms across the input terminals.*

Some ingenious writers manage an occasional tripling of meaning. In the Olympics of redundancy this may be worth a gold medal, like the 17-foot pole vault. One example of this athletic feat occurs in the sentence

> The aim of census analysis is to *predict* the *expected* population at some specified *future* date.

The writer of this sentence has inserted the idea of the future in three different words. It is just as clear to insert this idea with only one word:

> The aim of census analysis is to *predict* the population at some specified date.

6.1.3 Weak Word Choice

There are many ways in which faulty word choice can result in wordy sentences. Choice of weak verbs is particularly productive of wordiness. The weak verbs whose improper use should be avoided are those such as *is, has, does, is going to,* and *seems* when they are substituted for more powerful verbs. An example of such misuse occurs in

> The amplifier *has the capability of being monitored* at all times.

The weak verb in this sentence can be replaced by a much stronger verb with a resultant saving in space:

> The amplifier *can be monitored* at all times.

A flagrant example (from a student paper) of poor verb choice is

Sentence Criticism 85

> Safety matches *are* normally *contained* in a container but sometimes they *are* in rectangular boxes.

It is interesting to speculate on why this sentence was written in this manner. The answer probably is that the student who wrote it did not wish to repeat the root *contain* three times, so he deliberately omitted it from the second verb, leaving the weak *are*. It would have been better to search for a more accurate verb.

A second criticism of this sentence concerns noun choice. A rectangular box is, in fact, a container, so the second half of the sentence adds no information to the first half. All these items are considered in the suggested revision:

> Safety matches *are* usually *packaged* in folders, but sometimes they *are packaged* in boxes.

There are scientific and technical writers who prefer long words to short words. How this preference is first created is a matter for psychoanalysis. The result is usually plain enough on the written page, however. The page resembles, let us say, a scene on the African veldt. There will be a few striped and nimble prepositions darting about among great herds of hippopotamus, elephant, and giraffe words. The earth may seem to shake and thunder underfoot as the mass moves along, but such movement is, in fact, ungainly and deathly slow. An example of such hippopotamus phrasing is given by

> In this eventuality, there is likelihood of further land subsidence within the metropolitan limits.

A more nimble set of words gives the sentence lighter movement:

> In this event, land within the city limits is likely to subside further.

6.1.4 Use of Cult Words

Another stylistic habit which leads to wordy sentences is the excessive use by some technical writers of certain fashionable "cult" words. Examples of these technical cult words are *system, function, utilize, quality, accomplish, indicate, fundamental, determine, parameters, components, consideration, reliability, significance, technique, develop, evaluate,* and *potential.* These are called cult words here because, while they can have a well-defined technical meaning, they are often written with no attempt to suggest this

86

limited meaning. They are used instead to invoke the presence of certain windy technical gods who are expected to bless with success the description or proposal in which they occur. An example of such an invocation is

> The proposed *system* can be *demonstrated* to possess certain *fundamental qualities indicating* a *significantly* large *reliability potential*.

This statement does not have the sort of definite meaning for which the writer can be held accountable. Notice that the system (whatever it may be) is not presently in existence, but it can be shown to possess unspecified but fundamental qualities when it does come into existence (funded by the government). These qualities are such that they will "indicate" an unspecified degree of reliability in performance. There is no particular meaning in all this, but the gods have been invoked by the reverent pronouncement of such cult words as *system, demonstrate, fundamental, qualities, significantly, indicate,* and *potential.* Presumably they will bless with favor the journey of this paragraph to some contracting officer.

It may be argued that there is a need for such sentences when large contracts are to be won and preparatory research, unfortunately, has not been accomplished. This need may actually exist in an imperfect world. Still, the student of writing who uses cult words for what may seem to him a good purpose should not, in the long run, be taken in by his cleverness and use them to fool his own good conscience.

6.1.5   Trivial Statements

How do we avoid using long or unnecessary words or, having written them, how do we detect their presence? Some partial answers have already been given: Write with words rather than with phrases, use short words, avoid the passive, avoid empty cult words, avoid redundancy, choose strong verbs, and choose accurate words. A final suggestion is to avoid trivial statements. Making such statements is not a fault of writing style so much as it is a fault of technical judgment. One suspects that wordy sentences and phrases often result from the writer's lack of perspective with regard to his task.

Given a budget of so much writing space, or so much claim on the reader's attention, the writer should spend these funds where they are most telling, so to speak. Sometimes this may require the abandonment of certain small qualifications or scrupulosities of statement. More often, however, it requires that the writer abandon statements that tell how he got to a particular conclusion when the conclusion alone is of interest. It also requires him to abandon all the wrong starts he made and all the temporary words and phrases he used in constructing his thought (like scaffolding on a new house). If we set out to describe a mountain peak, for example, we err in making the first half of our report a description of getting over briers and boulders on our path to the top. This "briers and boulders" sort of defect, or, to put it another way, this reluctance to remove the mere scaffolding of a paragraph, after the structure is complete, is common with amateur writers, who do not wish to see any hard work consigned to the scrap heap.

The following passage, taken from a student theme, contains many of these Grade 3 2-by-4 and 1-by-6 temporary scaffolding phrases. The corrected passage which follows immediately after shows they are not all necessary once the main structure of thought has been erected.

FAULTY: The basic and fundamental elements of a typical radar *system* are the timer, modulator, transmitter, antenna, receiver, and indicator. The timer *is used to* insure that all the circuits *connected with the* radar *set* operate *in a definite time relationship with each other*, and that the interval *between* signals is *of* proper *duration*. The transmitter *as such* provides a narrow, high-power output pulse of r-f energy to the antenna *for a very short time interval*. The receiver, finally, amplifies the *returning radar* echo, which is then displayed on the indicator *portion of the radar set*.

CORRECT: The basic elements of a typical radar are the timer, modulator, transmitter, antenna, receiver, and indicator. The timer insures that all radar circuits operate in synchronism and that the signal interval is proper. The transmitter provides a narrow, high-power output pulse of r-f energy to the antenna. The receiver amplifies the echo, and it is finally displayed on the indicator.

6.2   CONFUSING SENTENCES

Confusing sentences usually are either incomplete or clearly illogical sentences. These faults of sentences will be examined here as they result from several possible causes: incomplete statements, faulty word choice, faulty classification, faulty modification, and faulty comparison. Sentence confusion due to distinctly grammatical errors (errors of number and reference, for instance) will be examined separately.

6.2.1   Incomplete Sentences (Ellipsis)

Ellipsis may be defined as the omission from a sentence of any words necessary to complete its structure. Ellipsis can be used properly to reduce sentence length when it does not interfere with understanding, as in *Connect the resistor to the diode when convenient.* The sentence, completely written out, might have been *Connect the resistor to the diode when it is convenient for you to take the time.* But saying all of this is not necessary.

Faulty ellipsis occurs when the omission of words leads to confusion or doubt. Writers usually commit this sin for one of three reasons. These reasons are (1) plain laziness, (2) extreme haste, and (3) a misguided attempt to write crisply and briefly. The first two of these reasons can be condemned out of hand. Haste makes waste, we can say, and perhaps laziness makes haziness. The third reason bears more scrutiny. How much can be cut from any sentence for the sake of brevity? Where should the scalpel stop? It certainly must stop short of cutting into the nerve of the sentence, which is its distinct meaning. It should not even cut into any meaty area—only into deadness. Those who are in doubt about any case of ellipsis should make their statement in full and be satisfied. Writing which is properly done must usually be done the hard way, sad to say.

In the examples which follow, errors of faulty ellipsis are displayed and corrected.

FAULTY: Concrete technology has made great advances and is now used in walls and roofs.
CORRECT: Concrete technology has made great advances and *concrete* is now used in walls and roofs.

FAULTY: No boat should be left without feeling it is secure.
CORRECT: No boat should be left without *the owner's* feeling it is secure.

FAULTY: Use insulation to protect against shorts and personnel.
CORRECT: Use insulation *to prevent* shorts and to protect personnel.

Sentence Criticism   89

FAULTY: When you have finished one half of the room, begin on the next.

CORRECT: When you have finished one half of the room, begin on the next *room*.

A special form of ellipsis can occur in the writing of titles, headings, subheadings, table entries, and in steps of a procedure. This is the intentional omission of the articles *the*, *a*, and *an*, as in *Classes of Elements* or *Turn off light and close door*. This sort of ellipsis is proper in its place. However, many writers fall into the habit of omitting articles from instructions in text in an irritating, completely random manner. An example is *Turn off lights and close the door*. To prevent this careless sort of hopscotch with articles, it is a good rule to allow such ellipsis only in a numbered list of instructions, or in some other circumstance where conscious control can be retained. In short, either use the articles in a consistent manner or omit them in a consistent manner.

A larger sense in which ellipsis in writing might be considered was presented in section 2.3, where "underwriting" was discussed. There, mention was made of the fact that a writer sometimes, consciously or unconsciously, leaves out key links of his argument, links which he considers obvious. This practice was compared to an artist's mistakenly leaving off the knee or torso of a human figure (which are obvious too). The writer should school himself to see his text whole, as the wide-eyed, innocent reader must.

6.2.2   Faulty Word Choice

Writers are sometimes astonished to discover that they have been spelling certain words wrongly, or have been using them without knowing their exact meaning. The manly remedy for both these errors is to admit the fault, look the word up immediately in a good dictionary, and recast the spelling or usage. It is a much blacker fault, however, to discover one has been using a word in the wrong sense and do nothing about it. Sloppy, inexact usage of words is a fault which, like driving without seat belts, people permit when they should know better. Here are examples of various faulty usages:

FAULTY: Death tends to *slow the population down*.

CORRECT: Death *reduces the population growth rate*.

FAULTY: The *affects* of such capillary action are not visible.
CORRECT: The *effects* of such capillary action are not visible.

FAULTY: The *speed trend* in airplanes is continuing.
CORRECT: *Design for increased speed* in airplanes is continuing.

FAULTY: The heart—that hollow, muscular organ of all vertebrate animals—acts as a force pump for the blood, and *is the heart of* the circulatory network.
CORRECT: The heart—that hollow, muscular organ of all vertebrate animals—acts as a force pump for the blood, and *lies at the center of* the circulatory network.

The last faulty sentence illustrates the fairly common error of using one word in two different senses in the same sentence. The first time *heart* is used, it denotes a body organ; the second time, it denotes a central position. *Heart* can be used correctly in both these senses, but surely not in the same sentence.

The technical writer must be doubly cautious when he deals with the specialized vocabularies of mathematics or science without having been through all the catechism which leads to a degree in these studies. Innocent-seeming terms such as *rate, acceleration, mass, velocity, weight, impulse, force,* and *potential* all have meanings dear to the scientist. These canny folk sometimes delight in trapping those writers who have blundered into a false usage. It is well for the technical editor who is not intimate with such ritual words to leave them alone, if he is called upon to judge them in some manuscript. Discretion is the better part of the editor.

6.2.3   Faulty Classification

A large proportion of English sentences are classificatory sentences. They say in one way or another that something is something else or is a part of something else. One such sentence is *Editing is a special skill of the technical writer.* Here editing is classified as a skill, which is reasonable. Mistakes of inexactness can easily occur, however. The writer, being preoccupied with the difference between such tricky terms as *speed* and *velocity,* may not notice that he has actually said something is what it is not. An example is *A bank is a means of monetary security.* The sentence classifies the bank as a means, which is inexact. A bank is not a means, according to federal law, but a place of giving and receiving money. Other examples of this sort of confusion in statement are given below:

FAULTY: The *operation* of a match *is* a unique chemical *device*.
CORRECT: A *match is* a unique chemical *device*.

FAULTY: *Sleet is raindrops* falling through a freezing air layer.
CORRECT: *Sleet is ice crystals* which have been frozen in a cold air layer.

FAULTY: Two *processes* to cool an engine *are air* and *water*.
CORRECT: Two engine *coolants are air* and *water*.

FAULTY: *Cryogenics is substances* exposed to extreme cold.
CORRECT: *Cryogenics is* the *study* of substances exposed to extreme cold.

Very long sentences are particularly open to classificatory errors. By the time the writer of such a sentence tackles the complement, he very often has forgotten exactly what he used as subject. An example of this, taken from a technical paper, is "The most highly critical instant of a lunar expedition is the time the astronaut first sets foot on the lunar surface and, over the period of a half hour or so, accustoms himself to moving about in this World No. 2 of his experience." The sentence actually gives the length of an instant as being a half hour or so, hardly excusable even in such unique circumstances.

6.2.4   Modification and Sentence Order

6.2.4.1   DANGLING MODIFIERS

Confusing modification is common in modern writing. It occurs most often when modifying words, phrases, and clauses do not appear to have an explicit verb or substantive to modify. Modifiers which suffer from total lack of a substantive or verb to attach to will be called *dangling modifiers*. Other modifiers, including single adjectives and adverbs, may be so far removed in the sentence from the word they modify that their usage is not clear. These will be called *misplaced modifiers*.

The most common example of the dangling modifier is the dangling participle phrase. The writer who leaves any participle in a dangling state usually assumes that the noun it modifies (most often a person) will appear somewhere down the line to claim it.

92

But often this person fails to clock in on time. An example is

Having turned switch K5 on, the control panel light glowed.

Who turned the switch on? We understand that some technician did, but this must be explicitly stated to be correct. It is an abiding principle of grammatical analysis that the analysis can apply only to what is explicitly stated, not to what is understood or assumed. There are two general methods for avoiding such dangling modifiers. One of them is to remove the person from the action entirely. *Because switch K5 was on, the panel light glowed.* The other method is to introduce the person explicitly: *The operator turned switch K5 on and the panel light glowed.* Dangling modifiers need not always consist of participles or participle phrases. An example of a dangling infinitive phrase is

FAULTY: *In order to learn proper soldering,* lessons can be taken in the shop.

CORRECT: *In order to learn proper soldering,* you can take lessons in the shop.

In spite of all the tedious good advice that has been given, scientific and technical writers probably will go on using dangling modifiers. This untidy result is suggested because such modifiers are a means of bootlegging human operators into reports and manuals while giving lipservice to the rule of impersonality. Onlookers of tests and experiments can actually be cloaked very conveniently within the folds of some ample, dangling construction. Many participles which serve this purpose have been legitimized in the past and now appear as honest "absolute" modifiers with certified parentage, such as the following:

Generally speaking, your data do not support your conclusions.

Taking everything into consideration, your conclusion appears to be unjustified.

Referring to your latest inquiry, the decision still stands.

Not counting the one on the pad, twelve boosters have been used to date.

6.2.4.2   MISPLACED MODIFIERS

Misplaced modifiers were described as modifying words, phrases, and clauses appearing so far removed from the modified word that their attachment is not clear. Adverbial forms do not suffer this sort of confusion so much as adjective phrases and clauses do. This results because there usually is only one verb per sentence to modify, but there may be many substantives to which a loose adjective modifier can attach:

> The astronaut ate his snack from a newly designed table *which consisted of crackers and cheese.*

Here it may appear that, to save storage space, the astronaut's new table has been constructed of crackers and cheese. The sentence must be corrected by making the adjective clause follow the noun to which it really relates.

> The astronaut ate a snack, *which consisted of crackers and cheese,* from his newly designed table.

Adjective clauses are particularly open to confusion when the clause does not immediately follow the substantive because some prepositional phrase, used legitimately as a modifier, happens to intervene. An example is

> The technician wired a resistor in the chassis *which was substandard.*

What is substandard here, the resistor or the chassis? It may be important to know. The sentence must be corrected to suggest one answer or the other. One solution is *The technician wired a substandard resistor in the chassis.* Another solution is *Although the chassis was substandard, the technician wired a resistor in it.*

Adverbial phrases and clauses theoretically follow the verb they modify, but there are so many exceptions to this rule that these modifiers can often be used correctly in several positions. This flexibility was discussed in 5.2.4. A careless misuse of adverb flexibility can occur with the limiting adverbs, such as *never, seldom, often, only, almost, even, nearly,* and *usually.* In many sentences, these adverbs can be inserted in any of several positions. An example is

> I *usually* come to supper on time.

Experiment will show that *usually* (which modifies *come*) can be shifted about. But when there exists more than one possible word to modify in a sentence, the placing of the limiting adverbs must be done with more care.   An example of confusing usage is

Texas Dataline *only* competes with Royal Specialties in the manufacture of servo controls.

Only, as it happens, can serve both as adjective and adverb. Thus it can modify practically everything but the punctuation. (Adverbs, of course, modify verbs, adjectives, and adverbs, and adjectives modify nouns and pronouns.)   Will the correct word or phrase please stand up and be modified?   Two possible specific choices are shown.   The first choice makes *only* an adjective, and has the effect of limiting the number of competing companies. The second makes it an adverb which is so placed that it limits the area of competition to manufacturing.   (These companies might compete, for instance, as manufacturing subcontractors but not as designers and developers of servos.)

Only Texas Dataline competes with Royal Specialties in the manufacture of servo controls.

Texas Dataline competes with Royal Specialties *only* in the manufacture of servo controls (not in their development).

6.2.4.3   SPLIT CONSTRUCTIONS

The adverb which modifies an infinitive is sometimes placed between the two parts of the infinitive; that is, between the preposition *to* and the verb element.   Examples are *to rapidly compute, to unhesitatingly choose,* and *to have rapidly learned.*   These phrases are called *split infinitives.*   Ordinarily, it is considered bad form to split any grammatical unit by insertion of a modifier. This practice of splitting infinitives has proved so convenient, however, that it is now accepted as proper when used with discretion. It is usually convenient when there are various objects and other modifiers following the infinitive and claiming precedence there. It is proper when the infinitive is not so badly split that it sounds awkward or ridiculous.

One other topic of outdated decorum is ending a sentence with a preposition.   The old-fashioned rule barring such endings can be disregarded.   The principal reason for this shift in viewpoint is that such final prepositions are usually part of a modern verb, created by combining an old verb and preposition.   Examples of such verbs are *set up, prove out, build up, try out, point out,* and *do over.* Ending the sentence with a preposition usually turns out to be no more serious than ending it with a verb.

6.2.5   Faulty Comparison

There are three logical rules to be observed in making proper grammatical comparisons: There must be present two (or more) explicit elements to be compared; these elements must be of a like physical nature; and the elements being compared must, insofar as convenient, be stated in like grammatical form. When the rules are not followed, the comparison can become confused. The exact degree in which sentence elements are to be compared is indicated by use of either a positive, comparative, or superlative form of statement.

Positive:	Diode A is *as* reliable *as* diode B.
Comparative:	Diode A is *more* (or *less*) reliable *than* diode B.
Superlative:	Diode A is the *most* (or *least*) reliable of all the diodes.

Here the rules for comparison have been observed fully except for parallel phrasing. To state the first sentence in an exactly parallel form would require something like *Diode A is as reliable as diode B is reliable.* But such a full statement is not required. Ellipsis of certain repeated words is proper in comparisons (though the syntax must be strictly parallel).

In complicated comparisons there is often danger of the parallelism getting lost in the scramble of explanations, as in the following examples:

FAULTY: The missile launch program is *as* complicated, if not more so, *than* the steering program.
CORRECT: The missile launch program is *as* complicated *as* the steering program, if not more complicated.

FAULTY: Jupiter is *farther* from the earth *than* Mars.
CORRECT: Jupiter is *farther from* the earth than it is *from* Mars.

FAULTY: Pluto is *farther from* the sun *than any* planet.
CORRECT: Pluto is *farther from* the sun *than any other* planet.

FAULTY: The *Australians* are as friendly as the *United States*.
CORRECT: The *Australians* are as friendly as *Americans*.

There are certain other ways in which comparison must be examined. One of them is in comparing or associating the items of two equal series. If the items of the series are to be associated in their sequential order of presentation, then use of *respective* (or *respectively*) is justified. A pointless use of this word (there is only one series) occurs in

> There are certain propositions in logic which are, *respectively*, either true, not true, or indeterminate.

A proper series comparison is given in

> Training courses for technicians and for engineers are to be set up in Building 2 and Building 6, *respectively*.

It is a common error to attempt to compare qualities which cannot logically be compared. Certain adjectives such as *unique, perfect, incompatible, essential, ultimate, final,* and *conclusive,* together with their adverbial forms, modify in an absolute manner and have no comparative forms. These words are what the computer engineer might describe as digital words (that is, two-state or on-off). Ordinary adjectives and adverbs, on the other hand, are analog words (capable of continuous variation in intensity of application). It does not make sense to say *more unique* or *more outstanding,* because these are empty classifications. *Most unique,* from the computer point of view, is redundant, and *least unique* is a blown fuse.

6.3   ERRORS OF INFLECTION AND REFERENCE

6.3.1   Classification of Errors

Errors of inflection are errors in the manner in which a word or word-ending is varied according to the circumstances in which it is used in the sentence. Since inflectional forms are tending to disappear from English, many people regard these errors as trivial, with possibly some justice. These errors usually do not confuse the meaning of a sentence and, at times, have even been known to provoke interest in it. The majority of engineers do not care whether *who* or *whom*, for instance, is used in a certain situation or whether it is proper to say *It is I* or *It is me*. These particular inflections are examples of case changes, depending in form on whether the noun or pronoun is used as the subject of the sentence or as an object.

In general, nouns and pronouns are subject to changes in form, depending on their usage as regards person, number, gender, and case. Verbs are inflected to indicate person, number, tense, voice, and mode. (See Appendix A.) Of all possible errors, only those associated with number (singular or plural) and with ambiguous reference (pronouns and some adjectives) are examined here. This is because ambiguity and the improper use of number can lead to sentence confusion, but confusing errors in such inflections as person, gender, case, mode, etc., are rare in scientific and technical writing.

6.3.2   **Errors of Number (Singular and Plural)**

The subject of a sentence and the verb must agree in number. Also, all reference words and their antecedents must agree in number. Most writers have no trouble at all with number when the subject is singular. But when plural subjects are introduced (particularly the compound plurals, as *time* and *tide*), then errors of the verb and pronoun begin to pop up like red huckleberries in the spring sun. This is particularly true in those very long sentences where the subject is forgotten by the time the verb appears.

Another possible source of number confusion is the sentence in which the subject and verb order is inverted. Still another is the sentence in which the subject appears to be compounded by some rambling, parenthetical modifier.

FAULTY: The *size and structure* of the typical snowflake *varies* widely in different regions.
CORRECT: The size and structure of the typical snowflake vary widely in different regions.

FAULTY: The fine structure and delicate design of the *snow crystal* are lost when *they fall* to the ground.
CORRECT: The fine structure and delicate design of the *snow crystal* are lost when *it falls* to the ground.

FAULTY: The *smoke* of so many factory smokestacks *create* smog in the basin area.

CORRECT: The *smoke* of so many factory smokestacks *creates* smog in the basin area.

FAULTY: In the test chamber there *is a shake table and a spray cabinet.*

CORRECT: In the test chamber there *are a shake table and a spray cabinet.*

FAULTY: The *electrician* (as well as the operator and the mechanics) *are* in the readyroom.

CORRECT: The *electrician* (as well as the operator and the mechanics) *is* in the readyroom.

FAULTY: *The group leader or his secretary usually take the call.*

CORRECT: *The group leader or his secretary usually takes the call.*

Some final rules must be added here to conclude this matter of number. Compound subjects linked by *or* or *nor* should take the singular, as witnessed in the last example. There are other special rules. When one part of such a compound is singular, for instance, and one plural, the verb takes the number of the portion nearest to it.

The indefinite pronouns, such as *someone, somebody, everybody, anyone, each,* and *either,* all take a singular verb, strange to say. An example is *Of the two alternatives, either is agreeable to me.*

The collective nouns, such as *class, group, membership, committee, pair, personnel, majority, department, team, crew, half,* and *many,* may take a singular or plural verb when used in their singular form, depending on whether the noun actually implies one thing or more. An example is *The group were split over the feasibility of building the new engine.* Since the group does not act as a unit, it is logically plural. The word *data,* used so often in technical writing, deserves special mention. *Data* is best classified as a collective noun, to be used in the singular or plural sense according to the considered judgment of the writer. A reasonable singular usage is *This data was transmitted by Mariner 4 from the neighborhood of Mars.* A plural use is *These data were received at hourly intervals by the Goldstone tracking antenna.*

The dispossessed singular form *datum* is still encountered. Occasionally one meets it with a guilty start in some corner of geodesy or numerical analysis. There, it seems to have a local meaning, implying a measurement or set of measurements suitable for use in numerical calculation only.

Pronouns and their antecedents (as well as noun and verb) must agree according to the rules of number which have just been cited. This includes the pronominal adjectives, which must be treated like pronouns. Examples of the pronominal adjectives appear in *these orbits, their errors, my turn, your move, that analysis.*

FAULTY: *These sort of transistors* are subject to overheating.
CORRECT: *This sort of transistor* is subject to overheating.

FAULTY: *Every person* should fill out *their* own time card.
CORRECT: *Every person* should fill out *his* own time card.

It is worth mentioning that when the gender of a collective noun is unspecified, it can be referred to with a masculine pronoun or adjective form, as *his* in the last example.

6.3.3   Errors of Ambiguous Reference

Every pronoun (or pronominal adjective) should have an obvious antecedent. This antecedent should be a substantive placed before the pronoun in some relatively important position. The normal assumption is that the pronoun refers either to the subject of the clause, a complement, or to an antecedent immediately preceding the pronoun (perhaps the noun in a prepositional phrase). Otherwise the antecedent must be some obvious word for which the relation has been well established earlier. Errors of reference occur when the pronoun appears to refer to either of two (or more) antecedents or when there exists no obvious antecedent. Reference is ambiguous in the following sentences:

FAULTY: The *company* halted *dish-antenna research* when it appeared that the Air Force no longer favored *it.*
CORRECT: The *company* halted *dish-antenna research* when it appeared that the Air Force no longer favored *dish-antennas.*

FAULTY: *Engineers* control natural *forces,* and my ambition is to be *one.*
CORRECT: *Engineers* control natural *forces,* and my ambition is to be an *engineer.*

FAULTY: *Harry's father* was wealthy, which gave *him* no happiness.
CORRECT: *Harry's father* was wealthy, which gave *Harry* (?) no happiness.

100

FAULTY: Good *servo designers* can usually troubleshoot *them*.
CORRECT: Good *servo designers* can usually troubleshoot *servos*.

FAULTY: He is a *mathematician* who knows all about *it*.
CORRECT: He is a *mathematician* who knows all about *mathematics*.

A detailed discussion of certain errors of reference, particularly with regard to the use of *it*, was given in 4.1.1.

7 *Logic in Writing*

The purpose of this chapter is to examine the principles of logical argument insofar as a scientific and technical writer might find them useful. No attempt will be made to present systems of symbolic logic, however, invaluable as these are in designing computers, analyzing contracts, creating specifications, setting up computer translation programs, and analyzing the structure of language itself. The logic to be discussed is the traditional logic of discussion, debate, and explanation.

7.1 TYPES OF NONFICTIONAL WRITING

To begin, we must first classify nonfictional modes of writing. There are four traditional things which a writer can attempt to do with his prose: explain, argue (or prove), describe, and narrate. Expository (or explanatory) writing attempts to explain the logical relations involved in situations, structures, processes, and ideas. Block diagrams are often used to accompany such explanations. Argumentative writing attempts to present doubtful, unclear, or contested points of logic or choice in such a persuasive manner as to obtain the acceptance of a particular point of view. Concluding statements are usually persuasive in tone.

Descriptive writing attempts to present the physical features of objects, structures, conditions, and processes. This sort of writing can usefully be accompanied by such illustrative aids as photographs and sketches and by tables of measurements. Narrative writing presents history, or a record of actions. It is usually used in giving the history of a program in a progress report or, in a scientific paper, in giving a summary of previous work in the field. The usual report will contain paragraphs characterized by each of the four writing modes, but scientific and technical writing is mostly expository writing. The two terminologies are sometimes used interchangeably in this book.

7.2 EXPOSITORY WRITING

7.2.1 Analysis and Synthesis

We are now in a position to study some of the logic of expository writing. How do we go about writing an explanation? Everything which we can conceivably try to explain, of course, has some organizing logic of its own, whether it be an object such as an automobile, book, or bomb, or a process such as skiing or flying, or a concept such as entropy, or a theory such as the binomial theorem.

This organizing structure is what must be described by the use of expository writing, and it must generally be described in two aspects, or in such a way as to answer two questions: (1) What are the lesser parts of this structure and how do they all operate together? (2) How does this structure relate to the world in which it exists? We must descend the ladder of structure of our subject to view the operation of its smallest elements; we must also ascend the ladder to view our subject in wide perspective as an element of an even larger structure.

For instance, descending the ladder we can view a computer as an assembly consisting of a logic unit, display, memory disk, timer, power supply, input keyboard, and program. Descending the ladder still further we can view it as an assembly of diodes, number- and letter-display tubes, power tubes, switches, transistors, memory cells, etc. Or ascending the ladder we can view the computer as an element in a missile guidance system consisting perhaps of a sensor, timer, computer, power supply, and actuators.

Descending the ladder of organization is accomplished by a process of reasoning called *analysis*, which means separating structures into their component parts. This process may also be called *differentiation*. Climbing the rungs of the ladder, on the other hand, is called *synthesis*, or sometimes *integration*.

Analysis and synthesis thus play a large part in expository writing. For instance, if we separate the traditional report into its subsections, we generally have the introduction, body, and conclusions. In the introduction we usually apply synthetic reasoning to relate our subject to the larger world in which it exists. That is, we attempt to compare the structure of our subject with parallel structures the reader might already be familiar with. In this way we orient him by relating what he already knows to what we want him to know.

In the body of a report we use analytic reasoning to separate the main structure into component parts for closer examination. Analysis is the logical process, in fact, by which we create outlines, tables, block diagrams, flow diagrams, classification systems, and various ladders and trees. Verbal analysis is the prose discussion which accompanies this process. This verbal analysis should not be confused with mathematical analysis (vector analysis, perhaps, or algebraic analysis), nor should it be confused with chemical analysis. Verbal analysis, as described here, means simply the breaking of a subject into component parts for further treatment.

7.2.2   Example of Analytic Explanation

The best approach to formulating rules for verbal analysis may be to present an example of verbal analysis taken from T. H. Huxley. The quotation which follows analyzes the logical processes of induction and deduction, which are presented in the next section. (Thus, the quotation serves more than one purpose.)

As Huxley presents his discussion, note how he offers first an example of a "sour apples" reasoning process, then breaks this thought process down into its unconscious elements. Next he classifies these thought elements under the two headings, induction and deduction. In accomplishing all this analysis, he completely explains to us the operating principles of induction and deduction.

Suppose you go into a fruiterer's shop, wanting an apple—you take one up, and, on biting, you find it is sour; you look at it, and see

104

that it is hard, and green. You take up another one and that too is hard, green, and sour. The shop man offers you a third; but, before biting it, you examine it, and find that it is hard and green, and you immediately say that you will not have it, as it must be sour, like those that you have already tried.

Nothing can be more simple than that, you think; but if you will take the trouble to analyze and trace out into its logical elements what has been done by the mind, you will be greatly surprised. In the first place, you have performed the operation of induction. You found, that, in two experiences, hardness and greenness in apples went together with sourness. It was so in the first case, and it was confirmed by the second. True, it is a very small basis, but still it is enough to make an induction from; you generalize the facts, and you expect to find sourness in apples where you get hardness and greenness. You found upon that a general law, that all hard and green apples are sour; and that, so far as it goes, is a perfect induction. Well, having got your natural law in this way, when you are offered another apple which you find is hard and green, you say, "All hard and green apples are sour; this apple is hard and green, therefore this apple is sour." That train of reasoning is what logicians call a syllogism, and has all its various parts and terms— its major premise, its minor premise, and its conclusion. And, by the help of further reasoning, which, if drawn out, would have to be exhibited in two or three other syllogisms, you arrive at your final determination. "I will not have that apple." So that, you see, you have, in the first place, established a law by induction, and upon that you have founded a deduction, and reasoned out the special conclusion of the particular case.

7.2.3   **Example of Synthetic Explanation**

An English geneticist and biochemist, J. B. S. Haldane, has written very simply and skillfully on topics which cut across the spectrum of modern science, from relativity to cell structure. The sort of reasoning Haldane applies when doing so can be called synthetic reasoning. In this process he gathers up bits of evidence from many sciences to establish some general result which applies equally to all.

In the following example, Haldane discusses physical magnitude and how magnitude alone can determine the internal elements of a living organism. His general conclusion is that every organism has some optimum magnitude for the performance of its function. Note how modestly and engagingly he goes about this very far-reaching argument. He is not, of course, offering a formal proof in this pleasant essay. He is attempting to explain or illuminate a general truth by showing how diverse examples all support it.

The most obvious differences between different animals are differences of size, but for some reason the zoologists have paid singularly little attention them. In a large textbook of zoology before me I find no indication that the eagle is larger than the sparrow, or the hippopotamus bigger than the hare, though some grudging admissions are made in the case of the mouse and the whale. But it is easy to show that a hare could not be as large as a hippopotamus, or a whale as small as a herring. For every type of animal there is a most convenient size, and a large change in size inevitably carries with it a change of form.

Let us take the most obvious of possible cases, and consider a giant man sixty feet high—about the height of Giant Pope and Giant Pagan in the illustrated *Pilgrim's Progress* of my childhood. The monsters were not only ten times as high as Christian, but ten times as wide and ten times as thick, so that their total weight was a thousand times his, or about eighty to ninety tons. Unfortunately the cross sections of their bones were only a hundred times those of Christian, so that every square inch of giant bone had to support ten times the weight borne by a square inch of human bone. As the human thigh-bone breaks under about ten times the human weight, Pope and Pagan would have broken their thighs every time they took a step. This was doubtless why they were sitting down in the picture I remember. But it lessens one's respect for Christian and Jack the Giant Killer.

To turn to zoology, suppose that a gazelle, a graceful little creature with long thin legs, is to become large, it will break its bones unless it does one of two things. It may make its legs short and thick, like the rhinoceros, so that every pound of its weight has still about the same area of bone to support it. Or it can compress its body and stretch out its legs obliquely to gain stability, like the giraffe. I mention these two beasts because they happen to belong to the same order as the gazelle, and both are quite successful mechanically, being remarkably fast runners.

Gravity, a mere nuisance to Christian, was a terror to Pope, Pagan, and Despair. To a mouse and any smaller animal it presents practically no dangers. You can drop a mouse down a thousand-yard mineshaft; and, on arriving at the bottom, it gets a slight shock and walks away. A rat would probably be killed, though it can fall safely from the eleventh story of a building; a man is killed, a horse splashes. For the resistance presented to movement by the air is proportional to the surface of the moving object. Divide an animal's length, breadth, and height each by ten; its

106

weight is reduced to a thousandth, but its surface only to a hundredth. So the resistance to falling in the case of the small animal is relatively ten times greater than the driving force.

An insect, therefore, is not afraid of gravity; it can fall without danger, and can cling to the ceiling with remarkably little trouble. It can go in for elegant and fantastic means of support like that of the daddy-long-legs. But there is a force which is as formidable to an insect as gravitation to a mammal. This is surface tension. A man coming out of a bath carries with him a film of water of about one-fiftieth of an inch in thickness. This weighs roughly a pound. A wet mouse has to carry about its own weight of water. A wet fly has to lift many times its own weight and, as everyone knows, a fly once wetted by water or any other liquid is in a very serious position indeed. An insect going for a drink of water is in as great danger as a man leaning out over a precipice in search of food.*

In reading both Huxley's "sour apple" passage and Haldane's "wet fly" passage, note how simply the explanation of difficult ideas has been accomplished by the use of homely examples. Haldane and Huxley were learned men, much practiced in writing, but they were also modest men, without that exaggerated sense of self-importance which leads many lesser men to write obscurely and pedantically.

7.3   **ARGUMENTATIVE WRITING**

The conclusion of a report is usually argumentative or persuasive in intent. The "evidence" which has been discovered and analyzed in the body of the report must be shaped toward some logical end in the conclusion. This end often involves making a choice, and the purpose of the argument is to influence the nature of this final choice. When the evidence is not conclusive, then possibly personal choice may enter, and the argument tends to become persuasive, as it is in advertising (the "Here is a message from your sponsor" sort of thing). But as long as there is a logical argument possible, then the conclusion should be drawn strictly on the evidence.

There are certain formal processes by which we can draw conclusions on the evidence. These processes, called induction and

---

*"On Being the Right Size" from *Possible Worlds* by J. B. S. Haldane. Copyright © 1927 by Harper & Brothers; renewed 1955 by J. B. S. Haldane. Reprinted by permission of Harper & Row, Publishers.

deduction, have fortunately already been described by T. H. Huxley in the preceding section.

7.3.1 Deductive Reasoning

Deduction may be described as the application of general principles of reason to a particular problem to arrive at a particular solution. It is reasoning which begins with general results and ends with particular results. In order to predict where a particular space satellite can be viewed in the heavens, for instance, we must apply Newton's laws of motion to the satellite at its present position and velocity. After completing a formal deductive analysis, we can make a prediction of future position. Mathematical deduction gives us our methods of simulating the physical world, usually with the view to making a prediction about some future state of its existence, such as the temperature or pressure of a vessel, or the position of a moving body.

It might be asked how mathematical deduction affects writing style. The answer is that, prior to the invention of geometry and algebra, all reasoning was verbal, and the techniques developed then are still in use in language today. The classical tool for verbal reasoning is the syllogism, invented by Aristotle and used by Euclid in the creation of his geometry. An example of a syllogism is

General Law:	1. All massive bodies are subject to the sun's gravity.
Particular Case:	2. Comets are massive bodies.
Conclusion:	3. Therefore comets are subject to the sun's gravity.

Statement 1 is a general law (sometimes called the *major premise*). Statement 2 is a particular case (sometimes called the *minor premise*) to which the general law obviously applies. Therefore, Statement 3 can be made in conclusion. (There are actually four forms of the classical syllogism, but the form represented above is the principal form.)

It is probably easiest for an engineer to think of the syllogism as being an example, in sentences, of the subtraction of equations. If Statements 1 and 2 are regarded as Equations 1 and 2, then subtraction should remove the common member of each equation. In the example, this member is *massive bodies*. The remaining term on the left-hand side (Equation 3) is then *Comets* and on the right-hand side is *are subject to the sun's gravity*. (Relating sentences to equations in this manner is convenient for illustration here, but the analogy should not be pressed too closely, in general.)

7.3.2   **Errors in Deductive Reasoning**

It often happens that we leave out the general law when we argue, taking it for granted that everyone knows this law. An example of this type of argument (with a suppressed general law, or suppressed major premise) is illustrated by a famous statement from Descartes's *Discourse on Method* (1637). Descartes begins his book with the deduction "I think; therefore I exist." The suppressed general law is *All who think exist*. This last statement may actually be true, false, or meaningless. It certainly invites a multitude of related questions such as: What does existence mean? Is thinking its only necessary attribute? Can any other attribute be sufficient to imply existence, such as movement? Does an amoeba think, and, if not, how can we decide whether it exists? Many of these related questions, of course, Descartes himself attempted to answer.

Other examples of reasoning by use of suppressed premises are available. Many can be taken from advertising. Take the old advertising slogan, for instance:

Viceroys—the thinking man's cigarette.

The implied deductive argument may run something like this (although there are various possibilities):

1. All thinking men smoke Viceroys.
2. I shall smoke Viceroys.
3. Therefore I shall be a thinking man.

This sort of argument, it should be noted, is not directed at thinking people so much as at people who wish to think of themselves as thinking.

It is easy to write a false syllogism by use of a misleading minor premise.

1. All birds have wings.
2. Bats have wings.
3. Therefore a bat is a bird.

Logic in Writing   109

The conclusion is obviously false. Perhaps the mechanism which leads to this falsity can be illuminated by use of a logical formula. Let A denote a group or class of things, such as men or birds. Let A_m denote a particular member of this class, and let α denote some quality or attribute we may wish to associate with the members of A. A proper syllogism then states:

1. Any member of A implies α.
2. A_m is a member of A.
3. Therefore A_m implies α.

The false syllogism should have made some particular statement concerning birds in its second step to be in proper form. Instead it took up an entirely new topic—bats.

7.3.3   Common Verbal Fallacies

The errors which it is possible to make in verbal reasoning have been extensively classified since Aristotle's time. Many of these errors have Latin designations, as will appear.

The Latin phrase *non sequitur* (meaning *it does not follow*) applies to conclusions which do not follow from the premises, though the premises may be true and may seem to suggest the false conclusion. One example has already been given (the false syllogism classifying bats as birds). Usually the phrase is used in a more informal sense, however, to describe any sequence which might mislead the reader.

> The lumberman's magazine will be published primarily for the working lumberman and for the general public.

In the example, we are led to believe the magazine has a restricted purpose until we are confused by mention of the general public.

The Latin phrase *Post hoc, ergo propter hoc* (meaning *After this, therefore because of this*) may be applied to both inductive and deductive reasoning. It suggests the common error of assuming that simply because one event follows closely on another, the former is the cause of the latter. It may be true, perhaps, that a lightning stroke causes a thunderclap, but it is not true that the flash of a discharged rifle causes the rifle report.

Another common fallacy is suggested by the phrase *arguing in a circle*. In this sort of deception, the conclusion is assumed to be true in the major premise, and then, like a rabbit from a hat, it is produced from where it always existed. The old funny-paper query "When did you stop beating your wife?" is an example. This, of course, assumes that you did, in fact, beat her. A more "scientific" train of circular reasoning might be the following:

> If we assume that the earth is round, we can conclude that all longitude lines must be great circles. But if all longitude lines are great circles, then the earth must be a sphere. This demonstrates that the earth is spherical, which means that it is everywhere round, as we set out to prove.

Arguing in a circle need only sound reasonable, as this seems to sound on first reading.

Argumentum ad hominem means *argument directed against the man*. It occurs when we say something to the effect: "How can he possibly analyze the motion of a satellite about an oblate spheroid when he doesn't even have a college degree?" The fallacy in this is that we have belittled the man without examining his analysis in any way. Our argument should only concern itself with his argument, not his education.

Another clever but shady practice is that of *begging the question*. This is seeming to answer a question, but actually avoiding it, when making a reply. An example can be found in the following exchange. "When can I quit working on this assignment?" "It doesn't appear to me you ever started working on it."

Another shifty practice is asking a loaded question. This might be a question which offers only two choices, for instance, when more are possible. An example is "Solar power is better for space applications than battery power—true or false?" The question is not so easily answered. Battery or fuel cell power must be used exclusively before the solar power panels are extended.

7.3.4   Inductive Reasoning

Induction is a creative thought process, not easy to describe or specify. One good attempt at description was phrased by Francis Darwin, son of the eminent Charles Darwin, in his *Reminiscences* dealing with his father.

> He often said that no one could be a good observer unless he was an active theorizer. It was as though he were charged with theorizing

power ready to flow into any channel on the slightest disturbance, so that no fact however small could avoid releasing a stream of theory and then the fact became magnified into importance. In this way it naturally happened that many untenable theories occurred to him; but fortunately his richness of imagination was equalled by his power of judging and condemning the thoughts that occurred to him. He was just to his theories and did not condemn them unheard; and so it happened that he was willing to test what would seem to most people not at all worth testing.

The example of inductive reasoning we are probably fondest of repeating (whether it is true or not) is that of the apple falling on Newton's head and starting there a train of hunch and theory leading to the law of gravity. Presumably the chain of thought led from study of the motions of overripe apples to the motions of projectiles, thence to the motions of meteors, moons, planets, and comets. It was Newton's very striking and original idea that one law governs all these varied phenomena: the inverse square law of gravitational attraction. Deductive proofs remained to be applied before Newton's inductive leap could be established as valid, but these proofs were possible once calculus was invented.

Probably the crowning proof of Newton's brilliant induction occurred when Leverrier, the French astronomer, deduced the existence of the planet Neptune from observed irregularities in the motion of its neighbor, Uranus. Applying Newton's law to these irregularities in a complex analysis, Leverrier predicted where Neptune could be found in the heavens at a particular time. The learned astronomers turned their telescopes there, and, to their astonishment, detected the new planet (1846). The chain of thought had come full circle. From observing the motions of known bodies, Newton had theorized the existence of a general law. Once the general law was established by deductive proofs, it was used in turn to discover unsuspected particular facts about planetary motion. The interplay of the two methods of reasoning is a rich and powerful one.

At one time there raged a hot debate in certain scientific circles about whether induction or deduction was the most important, most powerful reasoning process. One man who helped settle the quarrel was Alfred North Whitehead, a philosopher of science, who said, "There is a tradition of opposition between the adherents of induction and of deduction. In my view it would be just as sensible for the two ends of a worm to quarrel."

7.3.5   Errors in Inductive Reasoning

Inductive reasoning which is purely verbal is usually reasoning by analogy, or simply generalizing. There is nothing in either of these verbal processes, however, which guarantees a correct conclusion. A genius will use them creatively, somehow, and illuminate an unfamiliar corner of science or engineering. The man in the street will use them and buy the wrong stock.

Medieval scholars, having no tested techniques of reasoning, were overly fond of reasoning by analogy. An example of this erratic practice is the argument used by the church authority Francesco Sizzi to prove that Jupiter did not have moons of its own. (The church scholars, when invited to see these moons, would not look through Galileo's telescope.)

> There are seven windows in the head: two nostrils, two eyes, two ears, and a mouth; so in the heavens there are two favorable stars, two unfavorable, two luminaries, and Mercury undecided and indifferent. From all of which and many other similar phenomena of nature, such as the seven metals, etc., which it were tedious to enumerate, we gather that the number of planets is necessarily seven.

Sizzi thus "proved" that the heavens could not contain more than the seven known planets (including moons). This analogy probably seemed reasonable to most theologians, and possibly to most medieval citizens.

Another example of strange argument is offered in the writings of Francis Bacon, who possibly should have known better. In his *Apothegms* he proves by the following analogy that tall men are apt to be emptyheaded:

> Wise nature never did put her precious jewels into a garret four stories high: and therefore . . . exceeding tall men had ever very empty heads.

Bacon was either excessively fond of jokes or excessively short.

Modern instances of false reasoning by analogy are not difficult to find. They range from the plaintive "I didn't have to ground it when I plugged it in there. Why do I have to ground it when I plug it in here?" to "I'm going to vote for him because he looks like Abraham Lincoln."

7.3.6   Statistical Induction Processes

There are certain modern processes which can be described as *controlled induction*. Using statistical evidence, one can sometimes safely generalize from an array of particular results to a general result. From the statistically demonstrated fact that lung cancer is associated with cigarette smoking, for instance, health experts concluded that, to a very high degree of probability, cigarette smoking can cause lung cancer. This inductive result must in the long run be supported by deductive evidence to be conclusive. Possibly the fact that people still smoke indicates a distrust of statistical reasoning. Figures don't lie, it has been said, but liars figure.

Another example of a statistical induction process is election forecasting by polls. If a sample of voters is an accurately proportioned model of the larger body (in the political sense), then a poll should give an accurate forecast of the actual election. But the polling process must be conducted with extreme care.

We may state in conclusion that inductive reasoning is only valid when it is controlled with extreme care and when it is subjected finally to deductive checks. This sort of control and checking can be accomplished rigorously only by mathematical techniques. Purely verbal reasoning by analogy, or generalization, must be regarded as a stylistic fault whenever it makes large or important claims unsupported by deductive proofs.

7.4   DESCRIPTIVE AND NARRATIVE WRITING

The two forms of scientific and technical writing which have not yet been summarized are the *descriptive* and *narrative*. These are not of great importance as far as their logic is concerned. Descriptive writing portrays in words the physical aspects of an object, situation, or structure. It can most usefully be accompanied by photographs, sketches, and tables. Narrative writing presents a history (suitable in an introduction or program description). Narrative writing is also employed in scientific papers, summarizing

114

previous work done on the problem under discussion. Narratives are usually presented in a strict time sequence, and thus present no problem in logical organization.

Scientific and technical writing occurs seldom in purely narrative or purely descriptive form. Usually, as in trip reports and recitals of previous progress, the two forms appear combined, or are presented along with explanatory matter. The following passage is an interesting combination of this type because it relates the discovery of the electron. It was written by the noted physicist Sir William Bragg, as part of a book, *The Universe of Light*. In this passage, Bragg discusses the discovery of electron rays and the naming of the electron.

The electric spark has for centuries been a subject of interested observation, but no great step forward was made until it was arranged that the discharge would take place in a glass tube or bulb from which the air had been pumped out more or less completely. The spark became longer, wider, and more highly coloured as the pressure diminished. When Crookes so improved the air pump that pressures of the order of a millionth part of atmospheric pressure became attainable a phenomenon appeared which had not been previously observed. The negative terminal became the source of a radiation which shot in a straight line across the bulb and had mechanical effects. It generated heat whenever it struck the opposite wall or some body placed to intercept it; it excited vivid fluorescence in glass and many minerals: it could turn a light mill wheel if it struck the vanes. And, a most important property, the stream could be deflected by bringing a magnet near it. This was an extremely important observation for it suggested that the stream consisted of electrified particles in flight. Such a stream would be equivalent to an electric current and would therefore be susceptible to the force of a magnet. . . . Crookes believed that the stream consisted of molecules of some kind. He argued that his air pump had attained such perfection that the comparatively few molecules left in the tube could move over distances comparable with the length of the tube without coming into collision with other molecules. Such a condition, he said, was as different from that of a gas as the latter from that of a liquid. At the end of a paper contributed to the Royal Society in the same year (1879) he wrote in a dim but interesting foreshadowing of the future which was partly to be verified.

"The phenomena in these exhausted tubes reveal to physical science a new world—a world where matter exists in a fourth state, where the corpuscular theory of light holds good, and where light does not always move in a straight line; but where we can never enter, and in which we must be content to observe and experiment from the outside."

J. J. Thomson, Wiechert, and others showed that the stream consisted of particles carrying negative charges of electricity, and that these carriers were far smaller than even the hydrogen atom. The name "electron" was given to them.*

*By permission from Sir William Bragg's *The Universe of Light* (London: G. Bell & Sons, Ltd. New York: Dover Publications).

8 Organization of Written Material

INTRODUCTION TO PROBLEM

A story was told during World War II of two soldiers who stood on the deck of a troopship in mid-Atlantic, surveying the wide expanse of sunny blue water. One of them finally remarked to the other, somewhat in awe: "Do you see that ocean? It goes on for a thousand miles to the south, and a thousand miles to the north, and a thousand miles to the east, and a thousand miles to the west, and it's all just water, water, water everywhere it goes."

The other soldier considered this for awhile, then added some measure of his own awe. "And that isn't all, man," he said. "You're just seeing the top of it."

This story, being in the public domain, can be used to point up any topic the reader sees fit. It is suggested, however, that it be applied in the first place to illustrate the immensity of organization which must underlie the surface aspect of a report or book. The reader skims over the top of each page, seldom guessing at the depths of organization which must support the flat, placid print.

There is a second interpretation of this story which can be more useful here (perhaps the interpretation which the soldier had more nearly at heart). The surface of the ocean can be regarded in this context as an introduction and summary of its depths; it is like the foretaste, which every long document must offer its readers, of new and strange interior depths where the possibility of drowning exists for the unprepared. Every document, by this interpretation, has two aspects: (1) the introductory framework, in which we shall include the cover, title page, foreword, summary, and certain lesser pages, and (2) the "strange interior depths," or body, of the report, where an unfamiliar topic may be formally treated in lengthy detail, including long, analytical appendixes.

Planning the report introductory framework can usually be accomplished in a straightforward manner. It consists of choosing and arranging all the framework sections in such a manner as to prepare the reader for the watery shock of the body of the report.

Organizing the body of a report itself—or outlining it—is a creative act which must come from the writer's intimate knowledge of his subject. Outlining gives a simplification, a perspective view, a reduction in the number of dimensions. An outline can be compared to a fighter pilot's view of an enemy aircraft formation on his radar screen before he goes in to attack. The dancing array of yellow pips on the circular scan can outline for him, at a glance, a complicated geometrical problem. The radar screen, in effect, reduces space to two dimensions. A report outline should offer the reader the same quick, strong, and barebones coding. It should reduce the "knowledge space" to one lined-paper dimension along which the words of the text can be strung.

8.2   STATEMENT OF SCOPE

Before the outline is written, it is often wise to prepare a statement of report scope. The use of this scope statement can be illustrated by a case history. Let us say that some engineer has been assigned a topic about which to write and that he has done some research and study on this topic. After preliminary investigation, he grows impatient with planning and decides to start writing. Unless he knows very clearly what he wants to say and how to go about saying it, he often starts off in the wrong direction and quickly comes to a dead end, seeing no logical continuation. At this point he realizes he should have introduced certain vital topics earlier, and makes sudden, hasty, and patchwork attempts at rewriting, still without a clear plan of action. Soon after, at another dead end, he gets thoroughly disgusted, goes home, scolds the children, and then complains dangerously about his dinner.

In two or three more days he has wasted much additional labor and has been forced to cook his own breakfast two or three times. Still uncertain about where to begin, or how, he may simply quit in disgust, or may submit a botched, unhappy job. In both cases he concludes that in the future he will stick to hardware—"writing is what I became an engineer to get out of."

This is the unhappy result, of course, of poor planning. To forestall such an end, many engineering organizations require the writer to submit a statement of scope before the outlining and writing begin. The scope, as used here, can be compared to a statement of writing purpose, or to a thesis statement. What is the writer trying to accomplish with the body of his report? What is he trying to describe, prove, explain, or narrate?

A statement of scope should specify the limits of the writer's task and the means he will employ in performing it. The following is an example:

> This report establishes the prelaunch test procedures necessary for verifying that the Orion satellite on-board electrical and mechanical systems are operating within their design limits. The on-board systems are (1) the electrical power system, (2) the environmental control system, (3) the instrumentation system, (4) the stabilization system, and (5) the propulsion system. Prelaunch tests will be conducted in the interval from $T-30$ hours to $T-6$ hours by means of the automatic checkout equipment consoles located in Bldg. 26B and associated launch pad service equipment.

The statement of scope may not actually appear in the final report. Its importance to the writer lies in its usefulness in assessing report material. Like litmus paper, it can turn figuratively red or blue when it is exposed to questionable material, by this "color test" approving or disapproving the material for the report.

8.3   NATURE OF OUTLINING

8.3.1   General Outlining Sequences

Outlining a report can be useful for the following reasons:

1. It lays open for inspection the logical steps of the argument or exposition.

2. It insures against false starts by indicating where the text can best begin, continue, and end.

3. It reveals areas where more ideas or data may be logically required.

4. It chops up complex masses of information into workable units.

The question can now be asked—is there a straightforward procedure which the writer can follow to work up a useful outline? The answer is a qualified yes. The writer is advised to make his outline conform to any natural organizing sequence he may detect in the material itself. The natural sequences which scientific and technical writing employs are already well established. Probably all of them can be identified with one or more of the general sequences presented in the following list:

1. Sequence established by relative magnitude, importance, or priority of elements

2. Sequence established by formal logical process

3. Sequence established by time relation

4. Sequence established by motion or flow

5. Sequence established by operational steps

6. Sequence established by order of definition

7. Sequence established by random or artificial ordering

The listed sequences will be examined in detail in the following subsections. For the present, it should be kept in mind that the sequences can apply to report material at any level of organization. For instance, one paragraph may employ more than one organizing sequence, or one long report may employ one or several.

8.3.2   Example of Typical Sequence

Probably the oldest bit of engineering writing everyone is familiar with comes from the first page of the Bible. Our memory of it can be refreshed with a quotation (from the King James Version).

In the beginning God created the heaven and the earth. And the earth was without form, and void; and darkness was upon the face of the deep. And the Spirit of God moved upon the face of the waters. And God said "Let there be light": and there was light.

And God saw the light, that it was good: and God divided the light from the darkness. And God called the light Day, and the darkness he called Night. And the evening and the morning were the first day.

And God said, "Let there be a firmament in the midst of the waters, and let it divide the waters from the waters." And God made the firmament, and divided the waters which were under the firmament from the waters which were above the firmament. . . .

Study of this quotation shows that it begins with a pithy statement of scope: "In the beginning God created heaven and earth." Then it sets out to describe the manner in which the engineering of the earth was accomplished. It does so by selecting at least two sequences in the work and organizing the text, paragraph by paragraph, on the successive elements of these sequences.

The first organizing sequence is a time sequence (item 3 of list). The work described in the text is related to the seven days of the week. ("And the evening and the morning were the first day.")

A more subtle sequence can also be detected. It is that of necessary order in the performance of each operation (item 5). Chaos must necessarily be organized into land and water first, and time into night and day, before earth's creatures can be created. A table of operations might be set up somewhat as follows:

1. Separate chaos
2. Create light
3. Separate night and day
4. Create firmament
5. Divide water from firmament

It is clear that the sequences which have been listed will always have a certain interplay. For instance, the idea of time accompanies the idea of motion, and operating sequences are related to the logic of cause and effect.

8.4   DISCUSSION OF OUTLINE SEQUENCES

8.4.1   Order of Relative Magnitude, Importance, or Priority

Report order established by relative magnitude, importance, or priority of the items under consideration is best used when the report concerns some loose or merely formal grouping of separate

Organization of Written Material   121

objects, such as the planets of the solar system, the western states, the officers of a corporation, the duties of a maintenance engineer, or the commercially useful species of trees in a forest.

Julius Caesar began his description of ancient France with the famous phrase "All Gaul is divided into three parts." In this manner he introduced convenient subdivisions for the topic *Gaul*, and established some possible report subheadings. A modern instance of such technique appears often in the magazine *Consumer Reports*, which evaluates commercial products for sale in the United States "grouped in the order of their estimated overall quality, and, within each quality class, listed in the order of increasing price." This *Consumer Reports* organizing formula provides a method not only for determining the major report divisions (with respect to the order of quality) but also for subdividing these elements in another dimension (according to price).

The elements in the periodic table of chemistry are listed in the order of increasing atomic weight—hydrogen, helium, lithium, and so on to uranium and the transuranic elements. This method of ordering, devised by the Russian Mendeleef, was found eventually to reveal the structural subclasses of the elements; that is, the valence classes. Thus, one scheme of ordering will often suggest important schemes for further dividing the headings.

A last example of ordering by relative magnitude is afforded by the Saturn class of space launch vehicles. Descriptions of these launch vehicles are usually organized on the basis of the increasing weight each can place in orbit. The subheadings of each thrust class are then usually organized with reference to the launch vehicle stages (which implies an order of decreasing thrust). The following is an example:

Saturn I (Block II)	(orbits 10 tons)
S-I Stage	(1.5 million pounds thrust)
S-IV Stage	(90,000 pounds thrust)
Saturn IB	(orbits 16 tons)
S-IB Stage	(1.5 million pounds thrust)
S-IVB Stage	(200,000 pounds thrust)
Saturn V	(orbits 120 tons)
S-IC Stage	(7.5 million pounds thrust)
S-II Stage	(1 million pounds thrust)
S-IVB Stage	(200,000 pounds thrust)

122

The major headings appear, as mentioned, in a sequence of increasing magnitudes (weight in orbit), but the subheadings appear in a sequence of decreasing magnitudes (pounds thrust).

8.4.2 Order of Formal Logic

8.4.2.1 ORDER OF DEDUCTION

Report order established by the sequences of formal verbal logic (such as the syllogism or a classical induction) has already been discussed. The following is an example of informal syllogistic reasoning, which occurs often in the textbooks of mathematics, physics, and chemistry:

> The force which gravity exerts on a falling body is proportional to the mass of the body. This result can be demonstrated by a specialized application of Newton's second law. This law states, in general, that, for a body of constant mass m which is able to move freely, the acceleration a is always proportional to the force exerted F. That is, $F = ma$.
>
> Galileo's experiment, in which various bodies were dropped from the Leaning Tower of Pisa, demonstrated that all bodies fall equal distances in equal times, irrespective of their masses. Furthermore, the gravitational acceleration was a constant g, that is, $F = mg$. It can now be concluded that the force which gravity exerts on various bodies is strictly proportional to their masses, since m is the only variable on the right-hand of the equation. This is what we set out to demonstrate.

Examination of this sample of deductive reasoning shows that it follows the form as a syllogism (see 7.3.1). The sequence of ideas presented runs as follows:

1. Statement of conclusion to be proved (scope statement)
2. Statement of applicable general law (major premise — Newton)
3. Statement of result in particular case (minor premise — Galileo)
4. Deduction of conclusion

It is true that deductive sequences do not always run in this strict form. Sometimes the order of statement is varied and sometimes one of the steps is implied rather than stated. Still, the general sequence is used so widely throughout literature that it should lie at the heart of every good style. Shakespeare's Falstaff uses a syllogistic form of statement, for instance, in the passage which follows. In it, Falstaff is considering where Prince Henry came by his skill and valor in battle. The king (Henry's father) is cold-blooded and careful, so Falstaff reasons that Henry grew hot-blooded and valiant only through much drinking of a wine called sherris-sack.

Falstaff begins with a formal statement (major premise) that much wine drinking promotes skill and valor. Then he applies this general law to the particular case of Henry.

> . . . Skill in the weapon is nothing without sack, for that sets it awork. . . . Hereof comes it that Prince Henry is valiant; for the cold blood he did naturally inherit of his father, he hath, like lean, sterile, and bare land, so manured, husbanded, and tilled with drinking . . . good store of fertile sherris, that he is become very hot and valiant. If I had a thousand sons, the first humane principle I would teach them would be, to foreswear thin potations and addict themselves to sack.

If Falstaff's argument is stripped of its weedy verbiage, it can be paraphrased somewhat as follows:

1. Skill in the weapon is nothing without sack.
2. Prince Henry hath drunk good store of sack.
3. Therefore he hath become skillful and valiant.

8.4.2.2 ORDER OF INDUCTION

Inductive order always runs from the examination of particular cases to some general conclusion. It may or may not be followed by the application of this general conclusion to deduce some hitherto unsuspected facts. The following material has been organized on the basis of an induction.

> Study of the composition of the planets shows that the very large outer ones on which we have structural evidence (Jupiter and Saturn) are formed of lighter material than the small inner planets (Earth, Mars, Venus, and Mercury). Indeed, the larger planets are like the sun in composition, having many normally gaseous elements such as hydrogen and helium in their makeup. The primordial gas and dust cloud from which all bodies of the solar system may have been formed seems to have given up most of its gaseous elements to the developing centers of larger mass. This is reasonable, since the dust clouds, coalescing first, needed to grow larger than a certain critical mass before they could capture the freer gaseous

particles by gravitational attraction. The smaller planets never attained this critical capture size with regard to the nimbler free gases, and so remained relatively tiny and dense. The magnitude of the critical capture mass can be inferred by the following mathematical analysis. . . .

This passage begins with a train of particular observations about planet size and composition and ends by suggesting a unifying theory of planetary formation. The theory is not offered as the truth—more direct proof is needed. Still, a highly interesting beginning has been made, based on present knowledge. The organizing logical sequence runs as follows:

1. Statement of experimental evidence
2. Classification of evidence in significant manner
3. Theory of original formation process, based on classification

The quotation could now logically proceed to two final steps, as follows:

4. Derivation of general formula relating capture mass, orbital radius, etc.
5. Comparison of observed solar-system characteristics with characteristics deduced from formula

The elements of a complete inductive sequence thus always include a set of observed results, a significant classification of these results, a creative leap into general theory, a set of deductions, and experimental comparison.

8.4.3   Order of Time Sequence

Report order established by a time sequence is characteristic of histories, progress reports, trip reports, summaries of past accomplishments, and often of planning and scheduling documents. Significant actions occurring in the past (or planned for the future) are strung along a time thread, like beads on a necklace. All these reports are narrative forms of writing.

A strict time sequence is not often used to organize expository material or technical description. One exception is countdown procedures, which must proceed (except for holds) in strict synchronism with the clock. Strict timing is necessary since stations as remote as Australia and South Africa must operate in close concert during a countdown. (The countdown procedure may be considered an operational sequence as well as a time sequence.)

In the small sample of a countdown procedure which is given, a control system for spacecraft cabin air temperature and pressure is being certified for launch. Note that in such procedures there is very little need for skill in English composition. This is the sort of material, indeed, for which electronic data processing (with a simple catalog of commands) is adequate.

Time	Sequence	Con- trol	Oper- ator	Action	Verifi- cation
16:15:50	04-001	EC	CR	Press PRESS XDUCER to ON	E24
16:15:45	04-002	EC	CR	Press TEMP XDUCER to ON	E27
16:15:40	04-003	EC	CL	Press GLY PUMP to ON	E30
16:15:35	04-004	EC	CL	Press CABIN FAN to ON	E34
16:15:25	04-005	EC	CE	Record PRESS CABIN	_____ psia
16:15:15	04-006	EC	CE	Record TEMP CABIN	_____ F

An example of a purely formal ordering of engineering writing according to the days of the week was given earlier in the account of earth's creation (see 8.3.2). This organizing device at one time had religious implications, the number seven being considered sacred. But such a number also served as a convenient framework for memory, particularly when the material was taught aloud. (The modern student need not remember so much, having recourse to his textbook.) The ancient student had to remember a great deal, and, therefore, valued in lectures all mnemonic devices (aids to memory). Indeed, he may have characterized the best technical lectures by four qualities: clarity, brevity, variety, and memory aids, rather than by the first three, as we do.

8.4.4   Order of Motion or Flow

The sort of order created by motion, or flow, lies at the heart of a large proportion of scientific and engineering reports. This is particularly true if signal flow is put into this category (as will be

126

done here). In an earlier passage (1.2.4), the English scientist Huxley organized a description of the geology of the Atlantic Ocean on the basis of a fancied wagon trip from Ireland to Newfoundland. This organizing device of Huxley's was a pleasant, though artificial, one, suitable for informal writing. Signal flow, in a pinch, can be described as comparable to wagon flow, though it deals usually with electrical waves traveling across an electromechanical block diagram, rather than with wagons bumping across the bed of the Atlantic (*block* and *flow* diagrams here mean the same thing).

In general, reports dealing with electrical, mechanical, magnetic, fluid, nuclear, and sonic equipment, as well as with heat, light, radiation, and supervisory authority, can all profit by block diagrams. Everyone is familiar with their rectangular boxes, their networks and trees, and their rapid arrowheads diving in and out of the tangled lines like dolphins in the foam. Probably their area of simplest usage is in depicting institutional structure. In these cases, the president or project manager rests in a penthouse at the top of a subdividing network. Beneath this level, the network provides comfortable quarters on the top floor for all the vice presidents, or supervisors and lead engineers, and somewhere beneath them, for the assistant supervisors and system engineers. It finally wastes itself, of course, among the corporate "indians," who find no one at all underfoot in their basement cells.

But probably the area of greatest usage of the block or flow diagram in scientific and engineering writing is in the description and analysis of electrical equipment. Computers, radios, lasers, nuclear piles, autonavigators, servos — all these are subject to quick interpretation by its familiar line, box, and arrowhead logic.

The block diagram on page 128 describes a spacecraft attitude stabilization and control system in the attitude-hold mode. This electric and mechanical network is capable of holding a spacecraft in a fixed orientation so it can continue to see the sun, for instance, through a given window, no matter how its path happens to curve as it travels. (In other modes, such a stabilization and control system might perform complex rotational maneuvers.)

The problem is now posed for the engineering writer. How can such a block diagram help him to organize his writing sequences? Or how can a block diagram be converted into a good report out-

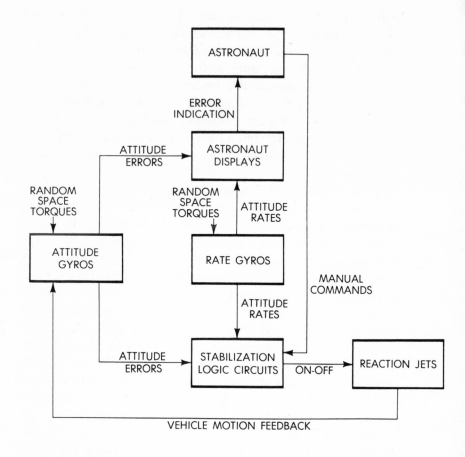

Attitude-hold mode of attitude stabilization and control system

line? Some general principles must be stated before an answer is attempted. There is almost always a point on the diagram from which signal flow can be assumed to start. Generally, this point is somewhere at the left, located at a box into which external forces send signals. Such an initial box can house a sensor or control element, which initiates action either automatically or manually. From this starting point, there arise voltage waveforms (pulses, perhaps, or modulated sine waves) which flow through the network by various paths, usually being reshaped as they progress

128

through each box. Somewhere at the opposite end there is shaped a final waveform which is used to initiate some useful action, such as firing a rocket motor or swiveling an antenna.

There may also be a feedback loop in the diagram. The elements of the feedback loop sense the useful action to check the manner in which it is actually performed. If they find that it is not being performed properly, they generate an error signal which modifies the original starting signal almost instantaneously to obtain a better resultant.

Feedback action is known as "closing the loop," and signifies stability of control. The disappearance of the hunger signal as one eats is an example of feedback control in a physical system. Presumably this sort of feedback prevents overeating.

In the flow diagram, the spacecraft automatic attitude-control network is not actuated until some random torque acts to rotate the spacecraft. This might be a meteor striking an extended vane, or even the unbalanced pressure of sunlight against some flat area, so delicate is balance in free space. How does the control network go to work to retain spacecraft attitude, or balance? The attitude gyros on the left (the attitude sensors) register the first slight rotation of the spacecraft. A coded error signal is immediately generated and sent to the stabilization logic circuits and to the astronaut displays. The rate gyros also provide information, not on attitude error but on turning rate, or, roughly, on the strength of the disturbance. All this information is taken into account by the stabilization logic circuits, which decide, in effect, which rockets to turn on to counterbalance the meteor torque and how long to leave them on. When the rockets actually fire, presumably they kill the unwanted spacecraft rotation. Feedback is effected by the attitude gyros, which sense all body rotation, including the restoring motion, and generate error signals until they are once more happy with the status quo. Since a manual override loop is also provided, the astronaut can witness the rotational state of affairs on his display and initiate electrical commands through his hand controls, if he pleases. Thus, both manual and automatic controls are provided.

How can this sequence of control be presented in a report outline? The usual method is to start with the disturbance and pick up all the control loops in one reasonable fashion or another as the arrowheads are chased down the network. The process is concluded when feedback (if any) closes the loop:

OUTLINE FOR ATTITUDE-HOLD MODE ANALYSIS

1. Attitude Disturbance Sensing
   1.1 Space Disturbance Torques
   1.2 Attitude Sensing Gyros
   1.3 Rate Sensing Gyros

2. Error Signal Utilization
   2.1 Astronaut Displays
   2.2 Stabilization Logic and Control Circuits

3. Control Modes
   3.1 Manual Mode
   3.2 Automatic Mode

4. Control Response
   4.1 Reaction Jets
   4.2 Body Motion Feedback

The control sequence which has been followed in this outline is a typical one: (1) generation of error signals, (2) error signal employment in control computations, (3) control action, and (4) feedback supervision of response.

When preparing descriptive text to accompany a block diagram, the writer should not try to explain in words what the diagram itself can display to better effect. The geometry of the diagram should speak for itself, while the text should describe or analyze only what the diagram cannot present.

It is a common fault of overly conscientious but unskilled writers to insist on repeating in highly complex wording what the diagram has already offered very simply. This is one instance in which careless repetition can lead to confusion. Such writers should be informed that many engineers study only the block diagram, so impatient are they with the text. They tend to regard the accompanying paragraphs as footnotes which they can rummage through only if they wish extended information. Ask one of these engineers how he happened to bump his nose and he will take up a pencil and work up a quick flow diagram, showing the geometry and all the vector forces at the unfortunate moment his nose was intersected. The only information he will not be able to pass along in this manner will be his emotions at the moment of impact, and

130

these he will display in a rueful grin. This anecdote can remind the technical writer how the other half of his world thinks—not with words but with diagrams.

8.4.5   Order of Operational Steps

Test procedures, handbooks, and operating instructions fall generally into the operational category of organizing logic. The shortest set of operating instructions which comes quickly to mind is "Close cover before striking." This outline for action was based on a need for operational safety, as well as for effectiveness. In other words, don't strike a paper match in such a manner as to ignite the whole explosive packet in your hand.

A longer set of instructions is the following, which, as it stands, offers a suitable step outline for an operating procedure:

1. Set brakes
2. Depress clutch and set gear in neutral
3. Pull choke out
4. Depress starter until motor operates
5. Set motor to idling speed by adjusting choke and foot accelerator position
6. After engine speed stabilizes, release brake
7. Depress clutch and engage low gear
8. Let in clutch slowly, depress foot accelerator, and start forward

The reasons for establishing this operational sequence for starting a car with "four in the floor" are inherent in automobile design. Any other sequence would damage the engine, the gears, or possibly a pedestrian.

A manual (rather than a procedure) discussing automobile operation would undoubtedly follow a similar sequence of paragraphs. However, the manual would require a great deal more explanatory text fitted in between the actual operating steps (together with block diagrams, photographs, and sketches). The passage from an explanatory manual which is given describes the use of automatic checkout equipment for a spacecraft. The figures called out in the examples are not given, the emphasis being on the organization of text. The student should note how explanation and actual operating instructions are continually interleaved in this typical operator's manual.

Organization of Written Material   131

The event-set switches are on-off switches, grouped in modules of four each, with an event command button placed at the bottom of the module and an event confirmation light placed to the left of the module. See Figure 7-1, which is a photograph of the complete module.

When the four event-set switches are set to some specified on-off configuration (for instance, ON-OFF-OFF-ON, or in digital notation, 1001), and when the command button is depressed, the coded event command 1001 is sent to the spacecraft. (Complete signal flow is pictured in Figure 7-2.) The event command is decoded by the spacecraft checkout equipment, and the proper event is automatically initiated there. This may be the closing of a relay to apply d-c power to the spacecraft bus, the closing of a fluid flow valve, etc. When the command action has actually been performed, the event confirmation light on the module (Figure 7-1) will light.

The actual steps for insertion of an event command at the event module will now be specified.

1. Set all event-set switches to the OFF position.
2. Activate the module as provided in Paragraph 4.3.
3. At the test conductor's instruction, repeat the complete command code aloud (as "F−1001") and enter it on the command log.
4. If no correction is indicated, set the event-set switches in the command configuration.
5. Check the event-set switch configuration with the command log entry.
6. Depress the event command button for approximately one second, then release it.
7. Report illumination of the event confirmation light. If proper confirmation is not received within 10 seconds, notify the test conductor "F module not cleared." Stand by for instructions.
8. If confirmation is received, clear the module by setting all event-set switches to OFF. Stand by for the next command.

The first half of this example is expository; the second half is procedural. The exact interplay of explanation and procedure in operations reports varies widely. Usually, test procedures, test specifications, process specifications, and countdown or operating procedures are all "procedural." Handbooks and manuals present both expository and procedural text, though the exact mixture must be determined by the experience and technical level of the expected user.

Introductory text in an engineering report is often ordered according to the sequence set up by a definition. In Chapter 3 (3.3.1), a formula was presented for the definition of a word:

$$T = C + d_1 + d_2 + \cdots + d_n$$

This formula states that a term (T) is defined by first classifying it, where C is its class, and then by assigning it intrinsic differences $(d_1, d_2, \ldots, d_n)$ to distinguish it from other members of the class.

An example of definition is A *trapezoid is a quadrilateral with two of its opposing sides parallel and two not parallel.* This definition has the profound property of reducing a complex geometric figure to a standardized linear sequence of words. Thus, it qualifies as an outlining sequence. An example of a definition used as the basis for explanatory text was given in 3.3.2, where the topic "Burglary" was treated in this manner.

Organizing an introduction or article on the basis of a definition is commonly practiced in scientific and engineering literature. An article on wine-making in the *Scientific American* can be cited for example. The introduction to this article follows:

> Wine is a chemical symphony composed of ethyl alcohol, several other alcohols, sugars, other carbohydrates, polyphenols, aldehydes, ketones, enzymes, pigments, at least half a dozen vitamins, 15 to 20 minerals, more than 22 organic acids and other grace notes that have not yet been identified. The number of possible permutations and combinations of these ingredients is enormous, and so, of course, are the varieties and qualities of wine. Considering the complexity of the subject, it is not surprising that perhaps more nonsense has been written about the making, uses, and appreciation of wine than about any other product of man or nature. . . .*

Note that this introductory paragraph to an article on wine-making follows the sequence of a definition, and the article, as it continues, follows this lead. However, other outlining sequences are introduced for special application throughout the body of the text, as will be seen.

*By permission from Maynard A. Amerine, "Wine," *Scientific American*, Aug., 1964, p. 46.

WINE

INTRODUCTION

Definition sequence. Defines wine as chemical, and proceeds to examination of basic chemistry of wine-making.

THE ROLE OF YEAST

Time sequence. Examines role of Gay-Lussac, Pasteur, and others in unravelling chemical action of yeast. Also *operational sequence.* Describes chemical action of yeast in converting sugar to alcohol.

THE EFFECT OF CLIMATE

Order of importance sequence. Examines effects of climates of France, Spain, Germany, California, etc., on grape culture.

THE GRAPE

Time sequence. Shows development of grape plant through history. *Order of importance sequence.* Describes varieties of grape plant.

WINE-MAKING PROCESS

Flow sequence. Refers to chemical flow diagram showing breakdown of complex wine chemicals.

WINE IN THE VAT

Operational sequence. Examines making of different wine varieties.

WINE IN CASK AND BOTTLE

Time and operational sequences. Studies wine aging process.

USES OF WINE

Random sequence. Discusses red wine and meat, white wine and fish, wine as medicine, etc.

The foregoing "wine list" should serve to illustrate the intermingling of various organizing sequences. The reader who searches out and studies the article in question will find that the mingling of sequences is actually even more complex than described here, taking place at every level of the text. The whole effect is rather like that of music, in which the various voices of the orchestra — French horn, bassoon, violin, bass viol, etc. — speak in linear sequences alone and chorded sequences together. The resulting harmony — difficult to analyze or outline — need only be clear and pleasing to be effective.

8.4.7   Random and Artificial Order

The telephone book offers an example of an artificial, purely formal organizing sequence. Telephone books, of course, list in

134

an alphabetical order the last names of all people who pay their phone bills. Whatever logic or reason there may have originally been in ordering the twenty-six letters of the English alphabet, there is none apparent now. Therefore, this type of ordering can be described as artificial or formal.

Random ordering schemes are quite common. The manner in which people line up in sequence at a ticket window is dictated by chance. First come first served, in other words, provides no logical sort of order. This is also the manner in which text is sometimes organized—first idea come, first written. Such random ordering of ideas in text is proper if the ideas are very few and if no logical grouping can be discovered.

One example of such ordering seems to be the Ten Commandments. These commandments appear in the following order (though not, of course, in the same words):

1. Take no other gods.
2. Build no graven images.
3. Do not take the Lord's name in vain.
4. Keep the Sabbath holy.
5. Honor your father and mother.
6. Do not kill.
7. Do not commit adultery.
8. Do not steal.
9. Do not bear false witness.
10. Do not covet.

Very possibly, Biblical scholars can discover a sequence here, but comparison with a modern penal code offers no immediate illumination on such topics as severity of transgression. Let it be sufficient to say that, for a list this brief, ordering as an aid to the reader is not always needed. For a list of several dozen items, on the other hand, some scheme of artificial ordering should be provided if no other is available.

8.5   **FRAMEWORK SECTIONS OF REPORT**

The discussion of this chapter so far has concerned the body of the report—"the hard part." The framework sections of a book or report can be written fairly easily, once the body is fixed. Most of these framework sections, listed here in their approximate order of appearance, can be found in any reasonably full technical document, but very few documents have all of them. (A few special sections, such as Index and Acknowledgments, are not listed.)

Cover
Contents
Illustrations
Tables
Preface
Foreword
Patent Notice
Proprietary Information Notice
Abstract
Summary
Technical Appendixes
Abbreviations
Symbols
Nomenclature
References
Bibliography
Distribution List

The manner in which the framework sections are to be drawn up is usually specified in the style guide of the organization for which the document is written. When a government agency such as the Department of Defense (DOD) or the National Aeronautics and Space Administration (NASA) contracts for publication of a document, these organizations, too, may require a specialized report makeup or format.

8.5.1   Preliminary Sections

The report cover may or may not bear the name of the author of the report and institutional approval signatures. This practice varies widely. When such signatures appear, they may signify that the report represents a technical advance in the state of the art, that the report commits the issuing organization in some contractual manner, or that the report discharges a contractual obligation.

The report title page ordinarily repeats all the information presented on the cover. It may also add information, such as a revision notice, authority for publication, and how to obtain additional copies.

In a short report, the pages which list the report contents usually give all the subheadings. In a very long report, these subheadings may be listed down through only the second or third order. (In the decimal scheme of heading notation, second- or third-order headings are preceded by two or three numbers; for example, *2.1* or *3.2.9*.)

The illustrations listing and the tables listing are made separately whenever the tables are organized in a numerical sequence apart from the illustrations. An illustration is usually thought of as a photograph or sketch. However, it may also be a block diagram, schematic, wiring diagram, map, or almost anything apart from the text. Sometimes a table is listed as an illustration, but usually tables are separately ordered.

A table may be defined as a two-dimensional array of words, symbols, or words and symbols. In this array, each "box" or entry must be associated with entries to the left or right, as well as above or below. A list is an array whose entries are associated in the vertical sense only, and is considered to be textual material. Illustrations, tables, and formulas (if they are set apart from the text) are considered to be display material.

The words *preface* and *foreword* are used in most reports in a synonomous or interchangeable manner. A foreword, of course, is a preliminary statement. Its most general use in technical literature seems to be in defining the auspices under which a report was written, as "This report was written by Satellite Corporation under terms of Contract AF11-089 with the Engine Procurement Department of the United States Air Force." Other uses for the foreword (or preface) are in offering a statement of report scope and limitations or in explaining unusual features or arrangements in a document. A typical, fully stated foreword or preface might read as follows:

This report was written under terms of Contract 4QS-11B with the National Aeronautics and Space Administration. Its original purpose was study of the performance of low-viscosity lubricants under high-vacuum conditions, but, on 1 January 1964, the study was redirected to include the effects of exposure to ultraviolet radiation and weak electron fluxes.

A patent application notice or a notice of proprietary information rights in the report is sometimes made part of a technical document. Both these notices must be legally worded, and can be inserted only by order of the organization's legal staff. Their intent, of course, is to protect the publishing institution's rights in any patentable devices the report might describe or in any valuable research information it reveals.

The report abstract probably can best be defined as a short report summary, made specifically for library or information retrieval purposes, though here again, practices vary. Often, this type of abstract is presented in library index-card format, ready to be cut out and inserted in a card file. The abstract which precedes a technical paper published in a scientific journal is usually written to inform the busy specialist whether or not he can find matter in the paper relating to his specialty. Thus, it does not present cataloging information, as the first type of abstract does.

The summary is usually designed to be read at more leisure than the abstract. It is written not to assist the reader in deciding whether or not to read the entire report but rather to replace the entire report. It may be used in this manner by the busy person who cannot go into report details or by the nonspecialist who finds the report heavy going. The summary is usually placed at the beginning of the report for use by these readers. When the summary appears at the end of the report, its value lies in consolidating and reemphasizing important conclusions.

8.5.2 Concluding Sections

The technical appendixes are properly a part of the body of a report. They may be considered extended footnotes, including extended proofs, extended explanations, and extended illustrations, which, if placed in the report body, would amount to trees getting in the way of the forest. All these trees, therefore, are best cut up as lumber and consigned to warehouses in the appendixes, where, if he is interested, the specialist can come on a tour of inspection. But he must be told these warehouses exist. Every appendix (there may be one or several) should have a distinct

138

reference in the text where its existence and purpose are made known.

Making up the lists of special abbreviations and special symbols (θ, #, Δ, etc.) usually presents no problem. The longer a report is, the more useful such a special list becomes, as it can obviate the need for inserting numerous repeated definitions in the report. This result is also true for definitions of special nomenclature (or the glossary). The glossary offers definitions for special names and terms needed in a long or complex document. Such concepts as *yaw axis*, for instance, and *pitch axis, origin, body coordinates, local horizontal, precession plane, color code*, and *standard gage* might all require special definitions in particular situations.

The list of references usually includes full identification (or citation) of all documents used as reference material in the text. Such reference listings can include the full document title, author's name, journal or book name, date of publication, publisher, page number, and other pertinent remarks which may be awkward to insert in the body of the report.

A report bibliography includes more than those documents which are referenced in the text. It should, in addition, include all other worth while applicable documents on the subject. Bibliographies usually result from an extensive literature search, and are a required preliminary to most scientific investigations.

Reports written under terms of a contract must often be distributed in a manner specified in the contract. The contractual addressees are listed fully on a report distribution list, usually appearing at the end of the document.

8.6 OUTLINE HEADINGS

8.6.1 Decimal Headings

Outline headings should have some sort of numeration associated with them to provide for easy reference. To be fully informative, this associated numeration should specify the logical order or level of a heading, and also should fix its relative position in the text. The manner in which the headings themselves are indented, capitalized, or perhaps underlined at each level of subdivision is often prescribed by a style guide. Such special rules for variation of the heading form are useful only where heading numeration is not provided. Where such numeration appears, the added variations in headings constitute a sort of literary flourish.

This textbook uses a decimal heading notation. The first-order headings are chapter headings. The second-order headings (7.9, for example) have been referred to as section headings, and the third-order headings as subsection headings (7.9.5). The few fourth-order headings (7.9.5.3) are called paragraph headings. The decimal heading scheme is the simplest to learn, and probably is the most widely used in procedures, specifications, and other rigidly controlled documents.

8.6.2   Numeral-Letter Headings

The standard numeral-letter system of heading notation is shown in the following example (rewritten from 8.4.4, with arbitrary lower-level headings added for illustration):

OUTLINE FOR ATTITUDE-HOLD MODE ANALYSIS

I. Disturbance Sensing
    A. Space Disturbance Torques
    B. Effect of Disturbances
    C. Gyro Signal Flow
        1. Attitude Gyro Signals
            a. Pitch Attitude Gyro
            b. Yaw Attitude Gyro
            c. Roll Attitude Gyro
        2. Rate Gyro Signals
            a. Pitch Rate Gyro
            b. Yaw Rate Gyro
            c. ... (etc.)

In this example, indentation of the outline headings has been practiced according to their order. Full identification of each heading does not actually appear before the heading, as is the case with the decimal scheme. That is, *IC 1b* is the full notation assigned to Yaw Attitude Gyro, and should be used in any textual reference to this point in the report. Yet, on finding this point in the text, the reader will encounter only *b. Yaw Attitude Gyro.*

The numeral-letter scheme, thus, is more unwieldy than the decimal scheme. However, it is considered to be more literary, and still finds support as an outpost of letters among the barbarisms of numeration.

140

SUMMARY AND REMARKS

A technical document must be organized both with regard to its framework sections and with regard to the body of new information it presents. A painter, by the same terms, must frame his canvas after he has organized all the colors and masses of the painting itself.

Organizing the body of the report requires creative analysis. The natural structural sequences of the material itself must be detected and put into correspondence with the report outline.

The natural sequences of scientific and technical writing were listed as follows:

1. Sequence established by relative importance, priority, magnitude, etc.
2. Sequence established by formal logical process
3. Sequence established by time relations
4. Sequence established by motion or flow
5. Sequence established by operational steps
6. Sequence established by order of definition
7. Sequence established by random or artificial ordering

It is probably true that many excellent writers do not go through a conscious outlining process when they write. Being impatient, they start to write at once, and, being skillful, they are able to organize the material successfully as they write. Other writers must actually see their thoughts on paper before they can wholly organize them. Still other writers can plan a successful initial outline and carry the writing through without deviating from it.

Using someone else's outline is helpful for small or controlled reports. For an original document, however, the writer should beware of using another's work. There is no more sterile approach to composition than that which tries to reshape someone else's thoughts. The ideas of others must always be considered, but they must be used like raw ore—broken down, assayed, and then made to give up their old identity in a fresh, new minting of information.

⑨ Criticism of Short Reports

The student specimen reports which are examined in the following sections each exhibit a different type of technical writing; that is, *expository, persuasive, narrative,* and *analytical.* Each report, furthermore, illustrates a different major writing fault, such as awkwardness, wordiness, poor organization, and faulty logic. The illustrations which ordinarily accompany such reports are not offered, the concern being purely with text. It may be complained that the specimen reports are all very faulty specimens. The answer to this is that they fulfill their purpose, which is to offer wide scope for comment. The good writer who may be inclined to jeer is warned that all his own mistakes are of the same nature, though they may be fewer in number and of less severity.

9.1 RULES FOR CRITICISM

Before we start, some rules for the game of criticism must be agreed upon. Mistakes of punctuation and spelling will not be inserted, since these topics have not been discussed. Mistakes of grammar will be made an issue. The rules of grammar are generally well defined in textbooks, and such mistakes are not a matter of debate.

142

Grammar must be clearly differentiated from style at this point. Style, for the purposes of this discussion, may be defined as the characteristic manner in which a writer exercises personal choice (such as word choice and choice of order) when he is at liberty to do so.   Thus, preferences in style are a matter of personal decision, and all individuals need not choose alike.   In the classroom, endless debate can ensue about the right way or wrong way to say something when, grammatically speaking, several ways are entirely proper.   Classroom critics often justify a particular choice by saying "My way cuts out two more words."   But this zeal for stripping sentences of all their foliage is evidence of some lack of perspective.   Clarity is a more important consideration than brevity, and variety in expression is a matter which must be judged over the span of several sentences.

The purposes of brevity in writing can usually be served more fruitfully by stripping a composition of useless clauses and sentences than by stripping the sentences of useless words.   The case is very like that of the Colorado River.   This river, in its journey from the Rockies to the sea, takes, at every point, the path of steepest descent.   This very efficient operating principle would seem to deliver the waters to the sea by the shortest route, yet the Colorado, like many rivers, meanders by long, involved, and tortuous channels to its destination.   Thus, in writing, the message may be delivered most quickly not so much by stripping useless words at every point but by considering the entire flow of sentences and paragraphs at the critical turns of their passage into meaning.

Style (or taste), then, is not a particularly rewarding topic for debate.   The Romans stated this almost exactly: *De gustibus non disputandum est,* or *There is no disputing tastes.*   The scientific and technical writer who is given some small choice should be free to exercise this choice within its modest limits.   On the other hand, if he imagines that he is free to choose when he is not free, then he should be called to account.   Using slang terms, jokes, and vulgarisms, of course, is not open to his choice.   Using newly coined words, however, presents a different problem.   Anyone who has worked on a highly active development project will appreciate that new ideas, new techniques, new processes, and new tools come to birth constantly, and new words must inevitably be used at the christening. These words, like babies, must be given a sympathetic hearing.

The demand for new words was particularly pressing during World War II. A partial list includes *stopgap, bottleneck, top-drawer, radar, bazooka, VIP, lobing, waveguide, staging, beach-master, amtrack, GI, spam,* and *flak.* Some of these words, of course, are no longer current. A modern dictionary can give the verdict on each.

9.1.2   Writing and Editing

The person who reworks someone else's writing is, of course, practicing editing, not writing. Editing, as a separate skill, must abide by a slightly different set of rules than writing. The editor, as presented here, is free to change the writer's words, but not his meaning. This rule is particularly important in scientific and technical writing. The technical editor often is incapable of judging content in the esoteric passages of technical literature, but he can, of course, judge inflection, organization, and syntax. The criticisms in this chapter will be made largely from the point of view of the editor.

9.2   CRITICISM OF EXPOSITORY REPORT

9.2.1   Specimen Expository Report

In the specimen expository report which appears below, each sentence is numbered for reference.

PAPER BOOK MATCHES

(1.1) A book of paper matches is a cheap, easy fire-starting method. (1.2) Paper matches fall under the general classification of safety matches. (1.3) This form of matches was invented in 1892 by an attorney. (1.4) From man's early times, such a unique chemical method was sought, and though paper matches aren't perfect, they seem to fill the bill.

(2.1) Although paper matches were unpopular at first and made by hand, they became big business in 1896 when a brewer ordered 10-million books to advertise beer. (2.2) This big order forced machinery for swift production in volume. (2.3) Today the industry produces 300 billion book matches annually in the United States, with over 90 percent handed out free to customers of cigar stores, hotels, restaurants, railroads, and other businesses. (2.4) This habit is not started yet in other countries.

(3.1) The primary reason all these book matches are passed out is advertising. (3.2) The advertising message is printed on the cover and it is read every time a match gets struck. (3.3) In addition to this cover, the matchbook usually contains two match combs inside with the match heads on them, also a striking surface and a staple. (3.4) Figure 1 gives a layout of all the separate parts.

(4.1) During construction of a matchbook, rolls of pretreated cardboard are cut by workers into combs of sixty match splints each. (4.2) They then have their heads dipped in paraffin and match-head chemicals, and cut to the desired width (ten matches is usually the desired width). (4.3) After the dipped combs are cut, they are inserted in the cover and fastened with a wire staple. (4.4) This process is sketched in Figure 2.

(5.1) When you use a matchbook, you have to strike the match on the striking strip only. (5.2) There is a good reason for this setup. (5.3) Part of the ingredients necessary to create flame are in the head of the paper match and part are in the striking surface on the cover. (5.4) Bringing these two requisite chemicals together in the presence of heat produced by friction yields a quick flame. (5.5) This flame is very hot. (5.6) It burns fast on the match head but slows up when it hits the paper stem. (5.7) There is a chemical—borax—in the stem which stops afterglow when the match is discarded. (5.8) Ordinarily it burns just long enough to suit the motion of a smoker in starting a flame, or the action of a housewife in lighting a gas furnace, then it goes out quickly.

9.2.2   General Criticism of Specimen Report

This specimen report seems to be a curious mixture of the student's own slangy sentences and of sentences remembered from his reading of a magazine or encyclopedia. The student's sentences are reasonably clear and brief, but his writing is not precise; and he has a bad ear, meaning that he cannot detect the roughness or inaptness in his own sentences as contrasted with the longer, smoother, encyclopedia sentences. Clear-cut examples of these encyclopedia sentences can be found in 2.3, 5.3, and 5.8, though suggestive phrases of this sort tinkle like bells throughout the composition.

In the first paragraph, the student's sentences are as loosely organized as gravel in a sack. Several preliminary thoughts are simply lumped there. This is a typical sign of starting nervousness—before the task of writing is warmed to and thoughts begin to come smoothly. It is to the writer's credit that he did not attempt to lump all these separate thoughts in one enormous sentence. Some inexpert writers think they have to button all their key points together immediately, so that at no point can it be said they have left anything out. This criticism does not mean that the ideas in the first paragraph are unsuitable. They include (1.1) definition, (1.2) classification, (1.3) historical reference, and (1.4) philosophical implications. Taken more smoothly, and developed over a longer span, they could have served as an adequate introductory statement.

The second paragraph returns to the historical survey and, though too brief, flows logically into comments about the present state of the match industry.

The third paragraph discusses the uses of advertising on matchbook covers, and then swings, in a very forced transition, into a discussion of matchbook parts. It is as if the writer, following an outline which includes (1) Introduction, (2) Construction, and (3) Operation, suddenly wearies of Introduction and takes the first convenient turn into Construction.

Paragraph 4 is technically weak, vague, and poorly researched. It is the sort of text furnished by the lazy writer who prefers to stay in the cloudland of general ideas, where he fancies himself an authority, rather than go prospecting through the hardrock of technical detail. What do all the clever match-head chemicals do, for instance? What makes the striking strip unique, what chemical decomposes in the presence of heat, what gives off the characteristic smoke and odor, what shuts off the smoke and starts the flame, what chemicals modify the burning rate and temperature, and what is the function of the paraffin's melting in a sliding liquid collar down the length of the splint? Finally, what remains in the burnt-out match head, looking like a tiny black sponge? Some of these questions might occur even to a child.

Paragraph 5 concludes the essay, trailing off weakly as if weariness, not logic, were forcing the conclusion. Indeed, no concluding statement appears at all, except possibly "Then it goes out quickly." The needed resolution can be provided by a summary statement, by a return to the opening statement for last comment, by a prediction of things to come, by mention of unsolved problems, or by some philosophical pleasantry.

146

A final general criticism which can be noted here is that the report has no subheadings for breaking up the text into logical, convenient units.

9.2.3   Detailed Criticism of Specimen Report

Detailed sentence comments about the specimen report follow, after which the report will be rewritten at the sentence level. This rewriting at the sentence level is typical of the work of most publications editors in a research and development organization. Faults of grammar, reference, diction, and awkwardness within each sentence are corrected, but, for better or for worse, paragraph content is not changed or rearranged by the technical editor, nor is amplification or additional research suggested or provided.

1.1   Poor definition: a matchbook is not a method. Poor terminology: we are discussing "paper book matches" (see title), not books of paper matches.

1.2   Vague statement: weak word choice ("general," "fall under").

1.3   Does "this" refer to *paper matches* or to *safety matches?* Also, "matches" should be "match."

1.4   Awkward, slangy ("fill the bill"); poor word choice ("unique," "method," "perfect").

2.1   Illogical (What is the logical connection between "made by hand" and "unpopular"?); slangy ("big business").

2.2   Too much ellipsis ("order forced machinery").

2.3   Encyclopedia sentence; abrupt change from clipped style (2.2) to smooth style.

2.4   Poor word choice: what "habit"? *Custom* is a better choice.

3.1   Slangy ("passed out"); faulty classification ("advertising" is not a "reason").

3.2   Statement too positive; needs qualification ("every time"?). Poor word choice ("message" sounds like a TV commercial).

3.3   Confused, awkward, dangling (a book cannot *contain* its cover, or even its striking strip and staple). Should be two sentences (the last phrase, "also . . . ," is too loosely attached).

3.4   Vague: what is a "layout"?

4.1   Puzzling: skips over too much of the process.

4.2   Poor reference ("they"): the workers seem to get their heads dipped and then cut ten matches wide.

4.3   Faulty tense ("After the dipped combs *have been cut,* . . .").

4.4   No comment.

5.1   "You" should have been introduced earlier; misplaced adverb (". . . *only* on the striking strip").

5.2 What "setup"?
5.3 Encyclopedia sentence.
5.4 Encyclopedia sentence; faulty reference (*these two ingredients* is better than "these two requisite chemicals").
5.5 Combine with 5.6.
5.6 Slangy ("slows up when it hits . . .").
5.7 Weak opening ("There is . . .").
5.8 Encyclopedia sentence.

9.2.4   **Specimen Report Rewritten**

In rewriting the specimen report in the manner of a research and development technical editor, we must preserve the exact meaning of the writer. The editor employed by a technical journal, it should be stated, usually has more scope than the editor employed by a research and development group. Since the journal editor usually works with severe space restrictions, he can suggest to the writer that material be condensed or deleted; or perhaps he can assign a total word count, leaving the chopping and pruning up to the author.

PAPER BOOK MATCHES

A paper book match is a small, cheap, and handy device for starting a fire. This match can be classified as a safety match (matches which can be struck and ignited only on a specially prepared surface). The paper book match was invented in 1892 by an attorney. This invention supplied a long-felt need for a cheap, handy flame-initiating device.

Although paper matches were expensive at first, being made by hand, they began to be produced in volume after 1896, when a brewer ordered 10 million books on which to print his advertising. This production order required the design of new, swift production machines. Today the paper match industry produces 300 billion matches annually in the United States, with over 90 percent of this amount being supplied free to customers of cigar stores, restaurants, railroads, and similar businesses. The custom of supplying free matches, however, has not yet appeared in foreign countries.

The principal reason why books of matches are distributed free, of course, is that they carry advertisements. The advertisement is usually printed on the outer cover where it can be read every time a match is struck. A typical matchbook contains two match combs of ten matches each. Besides the cover and the match combs, the book includes a striking surface and a staple. All these parts appear in Figure 1.

During construction of a matchbook, machines cut the rolls of pretreated cardboard into combs sixty match splints wide. These combs are dipped into paraffin and into head-forming chemical baths, then are recut to the desired width (usually ten matches wide). After the combs have been fully cut, they are inserted in the cover and secured there with a wire staple through the base. The assembly process is sketched in Figure 2.

Safety matches are designed to ignite only when struck against the striking strip. This design tends to prevent their ignition by accidental rubbing or bumping. The design is made possible by placing part of the ingredients necessary to create flame in the match head and part in the striking strip. When the two sets of chemicals are rubbed together to produce friction and heat, all the requirements for ignition are satisfied. Once a flame is created, burning occurs quickly on the match head, but more slowly along the match splint. After the flame burns out, a chemical in the stem—borax—effectively prevents afterglow. The paper match is designed to produce flame just long enough to effect the lighting of a cigarette or, perhaps, a gas furnace. Then it goes quickly out and loses heat rapidly. This valuable but free product of our times is as common and useful as the air itself—and perhaps as little noticed.

9.3   CRITICISM OF PROPOSAL

9.3.1   Specimen Proposal

PROPOSAL FOR AUTOMATIC SUBMARINE CONTROL SYSTEM

I. *Introduction*

(1) This proposal describes a three-year program of research, design, fabrication, and field test leading to the development of an automatic control system for submarines to be carried out under auspices of the United States Navy Underwater Research Department. (2) This proposed method of submarine control shall be planned to operate in six degrees of freedom underwater and shall be either manned or unmanned, the man-machine interface being planned to accommodate man in the most useful manner as a result of a human factors study extending over the first year of the contract.

The general program shall have four phases, namely, study, design, engineering model fabrication, and engineering field test. During each period, the contractor shall make visits to cognizant naval organizations for the purpose of requirements consultation and review of work accomplished (see Figure 1).

II. *Study Period*

(3) The proposed study phase shall investigate the application of modern navigation components to the underwater vehicle control problem, these components being stable platforms, high-accuracy gyros (attitude and rate), velocity and distance meters, and sonar navigating aids.

As a result of study of the capability of these components, automatic control networks shall be suggested for integrated operation of the submarine actuators. (4) The use of novel actuators shall be investigated also during this period, namely, jet propulsion devices, inertial attitude-control wheels, ballast-control loops, and variable-geometry wing and fin designs.

The submarine control equations shall be written in position, orientation, and velocity coordinates, together with variable attitude, thrust, and drag parameters, and the overall motion analyzed with a high-performance computer simulating a hydrodynamic environment. (5) General operational parameters shall be established as a result of this study, also the general level at which man can perform as a sensor and actuator.

III. *Design Period*

Overall performance capabilities and limits determined as a result of the preliminary study shall be used to initiate the design period. (6) At this time, submarine sensors, control loops, and actuators shall be selected, performance, accuracy, and reliability requirements on each element shall be assigned, and design of displays which can effectively integrate human operators in the control loop shall be effected. (7) Off-the-shelf components shall be selected at this time and design requirements on new circuits shall be specified. Complete design shall be carried out during this period, and weight and volume requirements in packaging determined.

IV. *Engineering Model Fabrication and Test*

The period of engineering model fabrication shall be used to produce component and subcomponent elements in-house, and to obtain them from appropriate vendors and subcontractors. All components shall receive extensive tests before their effective integration into the overall system, and subcontracted components shall receive extensive receiving inspection and acceptance tests.

Component interface control circuits shall receive extensive analysis and verification during this period. The final two months of the period shall consist of system integration tests

150

of the complete engineering model for the purposes of checking out design and apportioning final engineering parameters. Electromagnetic interference testing and human operator testing can also begin at this time.

V. *Engineering Field Test*

(8) Engineering field trials of the complete engineering model shall be conducted, during the last phase, at a test center of the U.S. Navy's choice, under the cognizance of naval scientists who shall oversee static performance of the system fixed in an appropriate study basin during these tests.

Dynamic tests will be performed as appropriate upon further determination of cognizant naval scientists. (9) These tests shall include installation aboard a submarine especially modified for the purposes of these tests, and carried out insofar as possible under dynamic operating conditions in a normal ocean environment deemed suitable to naval authorities. (10) It is anticipated that any further testing of the proposed engineering model control system shall be conducted as indicated by the success of earlier tests, and by engineering dispositions which can only be appropriately made immediately before these actual tests.

9.3.2   General Criticism of Specimen Proposal

This proposal is typical of those situations in which, for one reason or another, a great deal must be stated about little-known technical matters. The result tends to be a windy, vague, pretentious report containing many generalities and qualifying phrases. The fact that this is a student report does not change matters. As it stands, it is thoroughly like many actual proposals. It may be pleaded that the writer can do no more than set down qualified generalities before an actual study is made. This is true; even so, the writing is faulty for reasons which can be specified.

In the first place, the proposal is too wordy and contains too many long and involved sentences. Its rather stilted tone is evidenced by much unnecessary use of *shall* and by use of long words such as *cognizance, consideration,* and *apportionment.* The tone which these words lend was undoubtedly one of the aims of the author. Perhaps some of the long words are necessary, yet there are clearly too many of them for effective writing. The writer should have struck a more judicious balance between clarity and dignity of statement (if that is what to call the desired tone of the proposal).

If the truth can be guessed, this proposal might very well have been dictated. It offers the same sort of involved searching for meaning which a person goes through as he paces his office, declaiming to his secretary. The grammar and sentence structure are reasonably good for such difficult sentences. Perhaps the proposal engineer, when he finished his dictation, told his secretary to "clean up the fine points and give me a fresh, typed copy for approval."

One further comment: the proposal tends to run out of gas; that is, it becomes even more vague in definition as it nears its conclusion. This problem, which occurs frequently with study proposals, should be corrected; but such correction is an engineering rather than a writing obligation.

9.3.3   Detailed Criticism of Specimen Proposal

Almost every sentence in the specimen proposal is too long. Some sentences should be split into two sentences, others into three. Here are some detailed comments on the proposal:

(1) This opening sentence tries to state entirely too much. The unskilled writer is much better off trying to say something simple and easy at first.

(2) Too much "manned," "unmanned," "man," and "manner" for one sentence. The repetition is confusing.

(3) The sentence actually says ". . . period shall investigate . . ." This is inexact wording.

(4) This sentence offers a poorly constructed series. Presumably each item of the series is a *novel actuator*, yet the last item, "designs," clearly fails to qualify. Also, the series is too far removed from its introductory term, "actuators."

(5) The phrase after "also" dangles. Its attachment in the sentence is not apparent at first glance.

(6) "At this time," "during this period," etc., are monotonously repeated through here.

(7) Use of the passive voice also becomes monotonous through here. The effect is actually sing-song.

(8) This sentence seems to suggest that naval scientists are to be fixed in a study basin.

(9) Repetition of "these tests."

(10) What "actual tests"? Not clear.

152

PROPOSAL FOR AUTOMATIC SUBMARINE CONTROL SYSTEM

I. *Introduction*

This proposal describes a three-year program for the development of an automatic submarine control system. The program shall be carried out by the contractor under supervision of the Naval Underwater Research Department. It will consist of four phases: research, design, fabrication, and field test.

The proposed control system will operate underwater in six degrees of freedom (three of position and three of orientation). Human operators will be optional links in the control loop, the extent of their participation being assessed by a human-factors study during the first year. The four phases of the program are scheduled in Figure 1. At the beginning of each phase, representatives of the contractor will visit appropriate naval research stations to obtain operational requirements and to review work already accomplished.

II. *Study Phase*

The program study phase will be used to investigate the application of modern navigation and control components to the problem of automatic submarine control. These components include stable platforms, high-performance rate and attitude gyros, velocity meters, distance meters, and sonar devices. The integration of these navigation and control components with conventional submarine actuators (diving planes, propellers, etc.) shall be considered during the study. In addition, the study shall examine the use of novel actuators, such as jet propulsion devices, inertial attitude-control wheels, automatic ballast controls, and variable-geometry exterior wings and fins.

To implement the study phase, general submarine control equations will be written in position and orientation coordinates, with variable attitude, thrust, and drag parameters. The general control equations will be analyzed by a high-performance computer with programmed simulation of a wide range of hydrodynamic environments. General operating capabilities and tolerances will be established as a result of this analysis. A portion of the general study will simulate the use of human operators as limited sensors and actuators.

III. *Design Phase*

The design phase will begin when study results become available. Submarine performance requirements determined by the study will be assigned to selected sensors and actuators during this period. Control circuits to integrate these components will then be designed. Displays will also be designed to provide for integration of the human operator. Reliability and accuracy parameters will be assigned to the selected components, and weight and volume limits will be determined. Subcontractors and vendors will be chosen, and equipment specifications for all components will be developed.

IV. *Engineering Model Fabrication and Test Phase*

The fabrication period will be used to construct an engineering model of the complete system. Purchased components will be received and tested. Both receiving testing and functional testing will be used to determine compliance with the equipment specifications.

Component interface control circuits will be tested and verified during this phase. During the final two months, system integration tests will be conducted to check out and adjust final engineering parameters. Electromagnetic interference testing will also be conducted, and display adequacy will be evaluated by human test subjects.

V. *Engineering Field Test Phase*

Field tests of the complete engineering model will take place at a test center of the U.S. Navy's choice. Naval scientists will supervise static performance tests of the model system, which will be fixed in an appropriate study basin. Dynamic tests will be performed thereafter upon determination of naval scientists. Dynamic tests will include installation aboard a submarine especially modified for this purpose. These tests will be carried out, insofar as possible, in a normal deep-sea operating environment.

Further static and dynamic tests of the control system may be determined as a result of the tests already described, under conditions deemed suitable at the end of this phase.

9.3.5   Comments on Terminology

At many places in his text, the proposal writer inadvertently used different terms to signify the same idea. For example, "auspices," "cognizance," and "supervision" were used with essentially the same meaning in the original draft. The corrected text uses "supervision" more uniformly. Likewise, "apportioned," "assigned," and "distributed" were used to mean one thing; this idea

154

is represented in the corrected text mostly by "assigned." In addition, "phase" has been used uniformly for "period."

The difficulty with using changing, though synonomous, words in text is that the conscientious reader often assumes that the writer, equally conscientious, means to convey different shades of meaning each time. The reader is thus led to spend much time seeking genuine differences where none exist. After many such experiences, he may become grouchy and irritable. Some readers can be tolerated in this humor, but not supervisors or contracting officers, persons whom it is customary in our culture to keep in a good humor.

In general, verbs such as *determine, evaluate, test, verify, check,* and *analyze* and nouns such as *system, assembly, equipment, unit, set,* and *component* are especially subject to such loose substitution. The careful writer should have in mind a fixed definition for each, and should use it consistently.

9.4   CRITICISM OF NARRATIVE REPORT

9.4.1   Specimen Trip Report

It is often part of an engineer's duties to report on a trip he has made at company expense. This trip may be for gathering advanced technical information, for studying a field operations problem, for witnessing a significant test, or for giving instructions to a subcontractor. Whatever the reason, the engineer usually finds it his first duty upon returning to file a complete trip report. One week later, after he has finished submitting a detailed expense account, he may begin writing the trip report. By then he has probably forgotten much that occurred, and his trip report will be very sparse in details. Some engineers compound this forgetfulness with an absolute poverty of words when they write.

This poverty of words occurs in scientific and engineering writing as often as verbosity, and can be an even more painful problem to deal with. The specimen report is an example of a sparse trip report.

REPORT OF TRIP TO SPACE COMPUTER CORPORATION

This trip was made on 7 Sept. and return on 10 Sept. to report on programming courses. This type training provides our personnel with the fundamentals of their system. It reviews the type paper programs that are also being submitted with the hardware. It is required to review all such type programs completely by this company on submission for any vehicle. This review cannot be accomplished without software training first. It was coordinated with R. Dill of SCC prior to Sept. 7.

Training of operators shall begin on 16 October and take three weeks. It is on the level of engineers with digital understanding. Their computer equipment has four divisions: input-output, memory, command-control, and arithmetic, each half a week.

The review of software is one week. The software has the computer update the displays. The test vehicle feeds all information and the computer selects what it wants for the display. New software tapes to program the computer for new type displays can be entered in five minutes, and a tape library is needed of about 200 tapes. It is recommended that six personnel are sent for the course on 16 October and six more in three weeks. For information call E. Kachin.

9.4.2 Criticism of Specimen Trip Report

This writer seems reasonably intelligent, yet his writing is very poor. Some of the most flagrant mistakes are (1) hasty, elliptical composition, (2) faulty sequence of ideas, (3) careless presentation of important points, and (4) poor subordination of secondary points.

What causes a writer to perform in this manner? If one psychological defect is to be named, it may be that of mental laziness in dealing with words. The writer seems to prefer setting down pleasant vignettes of his trip as they come to mind, rather than working at shaping these random impressions into a complete, directed pattern of thought.

The engineer may be peculiarly open to this temptation, with his tendency to think in geometrical rather than in verbal terms. That is, he may prefer simply hopping about his mental concept, picking phrases, tags, and labels off here and there for verbal transmission, like a bird hopping about a berry bush. People who hop about their mental concepts in this birdlike manner tend to think that other people have an identical picture gallery in their heads — why not? They think they need only identify a picture to call it forth for the reader — not actually describe it to him. They do not realize that writing and reading constitute a creative "rebirth" process, not an identification process.

The specimen trip report will not be commented upon sentence by sentence; it will be rewritten. To produce a meaningful revision, it was necessary to organize the report in conventional narrative form (time-sequenced), with a short introduction. It was also necessary to read between the lines, guessing in some cases at what was meant. Thus, this particular revision requires both editing and engineering skill.

9.4.3   Specimen Trip Report Rewritten

REPORT OF TRIP TO SPACE COMPUTER CORPORATION

Between 7 September and 10 September, the writer visited Space Computer Corporation to review their space-computer operator training course. This review was necessary for two reasons. The first reason was that our own personnel will be attending this course to gain familiarity with the space computer, which is to be used in our Orion spacecraft. The second reason was that we must be prepared to review and criticize certain computer software (display programming tapes) to be purchased separately from the computer.

The writer examined the computer study course and found that it was organized on a three-week basis, the first session beginning on 16 October. Prerequisites for students attending the course are a familiarity with digital notation and acquaintance with digital circuit design.

The first two weeks of the course will be spent on computer fundamentals. These include (1) input-output methods, (2) memory registers, (3) command control, and (4) arithmetic computation; one-half week will be devoted to study of each item. The last week of the course will be spent on display tape preparation. This is the software necessary to program the computer to address and command the various spacecraft displays. Different tapes for different computing functions can be entered in the computer memory in about five minutes. A large tape library will be required eventually to process all available spacecraft data, and these tapes need careful review to determine whether they fulfill our needs.

As a result of this trip, it is recommended that six of our personnel attend the first computer training session beginning on 16 October and that six more attend the second session beginning three weeks later. Arrangements to attend can be handled through R. Dill of SCC, who also coordinated the writer's visit. Additional information can be obtained by calling the writer, E. Kachin.

CRITICISM OF ANALYTICAL REPORT

9.5.1   **Specimen Analytical Report**

A specimen report is presented next, giving a rather vague and incomplete analysis of population trends. The five steps of a proper inductive-deductive sequence were listed earlier (8.4.2.2), and these are repeated below for review and application to the specimen report.

1. Presentation of factual data
2. Classification of data in significant manner
3. Statement of theory suggested by classification
4. Application of theory to particular case
5. Prediction of particular result

AMERICAN POPULATION TRENDS

Introduction

(1) Population studies have been conducted by many nations since ancient times. References have been found in the records of old Hebrews and Romans concerning population counts. (2) Their reasons for their counts were different than we have today; the number of their population was of secondary importance, their primary purpose being to know who to tax and who to conscript for the army. Population is defined as the number of people or, in statistical terms, the number of individuals or items appearing in a total count. (3) This is the sense in which we know it today.

Data Source

The data on population presented in this report are all from the U.S. Government census which has been taken every ten years since 1790. The government census is the only complete count of the population and, therefore, is the primary data source for all population studies. The data includes counts for Alaska and Hawaii for 1950 and 1960, and includes American military personnel overseas. Results since 1920 are presented in Table 1. (4) This table is very interesting for planners because all planning should begin with such knowledge if it is to be realistic.

TABLE 1. U.S. POPULATION GROWTH

YEAR	POPULATION
1920	105,710,620
1930	122,775,046
1940	131,669,275
1950	150,679,361
1960	178,464,236

Conclusion

The population of the United States shows a steady increase. This increase can readily be noted in Table 1. (5) Therefore it seems reasonable to project the population ahead whenever we want to know the future. This table can even be used for planning schools, roads, pension programs, tax income, welfare services, food, and similar items. (6) The census is also used to apportion the U.S. House of Representatives, each electoral district having by law approximately 1/435 of the total U.S. population.

(7) Actually, only about six percent of the world's population are U.S. citizens. The nations of India, China, and Russia have larger populations. The actual population ranking of the first dozen nations is (1) China, (2) India, (3) Russia, (4) United States, (5) Japan, (6) Indonesia, (7) Pakistan, (8) Germany, (9) Brazil, (10) United Kingdom, (11) Italy, and (12) France.

World population has been gaining enormously lately, and a population explosion is threatened unless mass birth control of some sort is practiced soon throughout the world. The number of new inhabitants added to the United States between 1950 and 1960, for instance, was almost exactly equal to the growth between 1790 and 1863.

9.5.2   Criticism of Specimen Report

This is a pleasant but wandering report on population "trends." Its style is sometimes awkward, principally because the writer, not seeming to know what he wants to do, makes abrupt, awkward changes in the direction of his argument. Also, the style is often colloquial; that is, more suited to speaking than to writing. The report might be suitable as idle reading of the Sunday-supplement variety, but as a technical report—an instrument, that is, by which some of the chaos of nature is mapped and ordered—it suffers complete failure. A person who writes in this manner probably has little knowledge of the actual procedures of science or engineering.

Some detailed sentence comments are:

(1) It seems to be a common habit of the wandering type of report to start with a reference to ancient history.

(2) The reason we count population should be explicitly stated; also, the sentence is long and awkwardly constructed; "different than" is improper usage; use *whom* instead of "who."

(3) The sense, or definition, of the term "population" was undoubtedly the same for the Hebrews as it is for us. The

Hebrews' reasons for taking a census may have differed from ours. This idea is not made clear.

(4) The table is more than interesting. It can offer a significant classification of population data; that is, it can serve as an analytical tool (as will be shown).

(5) Uses for the table are suggested but never followed up.

(6) This sentence gives the legal reason for taking a population count, and should be introduced earlier.

(7) For a while it appeared that the report would offer some real analysis, but here it starts to wander again, offering merely curious material.

In the next subsection, the specimen report is rewritten in such a way as to give it a purpose. This shaping required removing extraneous material and adding other material. A statement of purpose, or scope, is made early, according to which the remainder of the report is shaped. An inductive-deductive outline was followed.

9.5.3 Analytical Report Rewritten

AMERICAN POPULATION TRENDS

Introduction

It is useful to make forecasts of the American population, because this information is vital in national planning. This report will attempt to make such a forecast for 1970. This forecast can provide a basis for the orderly expansion of governmental and private financing of all kinds leading into that period.

The U.S. Bureau of the Census was established to provide a basis for apportionment of the House of Representatives of the U.S. Congress. However, in modern times, the elaborate statistics provided by the Census Bureau are also used in planning schools, roads, welfare services, food supplies, tax income, etc. Thus, the need for an accurate periodic census has increased as the nation has grown.

Population is defined as the total number of persons residing in an area at the time the count is taken. The U.S. Census, in addition, includes military personnel living overseas and, since 1950, the people of Alaska and Hawaii.

Classification of Data

The population of the United States from 1920 through 1960 is presented in Table 1, as gathered by each decennial census. The percentage increase is shown for each period also, as well as a forecast for the 1970 census.

TABLE 1. U.S. POPULATION GROWTH

YEAR	POPULATION	PERCENT INCREASE
1920	105,710,620	. . .
1930	122,775,046	16.1
1940	131,669,275	7.2
1950	150,679,361	14.5
1960	178,464,236	18.4
1970	203,627,500 (predicted)	14.1 (average)

This table is interesting because it shows a fairly uniform increase of population over the period cited. The effects of the depression appear in the small increase noted for 1930 to 1940. The effects of war and the subsequent population boom can be noted for the period 1950 to 1960. Barring war, depression, famine, and other unpredictable disasters, then, it can be stated that a 14.1-percent population increase over the decennial period 1960 to 1970 is a reasonable expectation.

Conclusion

If our average population growth of 14.1 percent every decennial period is projected to 1970, our population then will be 203,627,-500. This prediction can be refined, of course, by more elaborate calculating techniques.

The average increase may not seem large in terms of percentage, but when the percentage is applied to our present population base, it becomes far more striking. Other studies show that the entire world is undergoing a population explosion, and the United States appears to be participating in it. Indeed, the growth of the U.S. population between 1950 and 1960 alone was almost equal to the total growth between 1790 and 1863. Birth control measures of some kind may be required in the near future.

$\widehat{10}$ *Program Documentation Requirements*

10.1   DOCUMENTATION SURVEY

There are perhaps 60,000 genuine scientific and technical journals published throughout the world. The total number of papers published is perhaps 1,500,000 each year. This does not include the output of trade publishers, book and monograph publishers, small professional societies, and students.

The scientific and technical copy published by research and development organizations is also large. One corporation alone publishes at least 60,000,000 words of report and manual master copy each year.

The greatest number of professional technical writers are employed to write reports and manuals. Many scientists and engineers, of course, do not write directly for money. Their writing for the journals is a labor of love. Still, at one time or another, all of them may be required to contribute to documents of the types to be discussed. These include proposals, planning reports, specifications, investigation reports, quality control and reliability reports, test reports, progress reports, procedures, handbooks, and manuals.

The usual reverence which attaches to a million or billion American dollars is not meant to be invoked here, however. It is suggested that any awe which the student can manage be directed to appreciation of these report types as artifacts of a highly technical civilization. Like the handsaw, the storage battery, and the laser, they are the tools we employ in doing our technical business. A thousand years from now they may be museum pieces, telling our descendants how we created the sparkling new worlds of the moon and Mars. Even now they bear the use-polished stamp of all goods tools, rounded to serve purely functional ends, curved to fit the shapes of our hands and our thoughts.

For the purposes of outlining, the reports discussed in this chapter follow the natural sequence in which they become important as a technical program develops. Let us assume, for instance, that a large governmental agency such as NASA has begun the report cycle by asking the aerospace industry for study proposals for the development of an advanced space system, such as a manned orbiting laboratory. If the program continues to be funded, then the proposal stage will flow into the planning stage with its planning reports, plans will flow into specifications, and so on. There is, in fact, an organic growth connected with the whole report apparatus, which will be seen as the discussion progresses.

The funded report types to be discussed do not, however, include all areas of corporate technical writing. Company product brochures will not be discussed, nor public information reports, film writing, briefings, oral presentations, and letters.

10.2   PROPOSALS

10.2.1   Study Proposals

Study proposals may be funded for all types of contractual research and development. They are usually solicited by a governmental agency (though sometimes by corporations). When NASA, for instance, requires studies leading to the development of new equipment, it usually prepares and circulates among interested contractors a request for a study proposal. This request is usually a standard statement specifying desirable system operating parameters. It also specifies the study period and the funding to be awarded.

The corporations or institutions invited to respond are asked to propose how they would go about making the study. The agency study team then evaluates each proposal, normally on the basis of

Program Documentation Requirements   163

demonstrated technical excellence. Finally the agency gives one or more of the contractors an award to perform a study, based on the proposal.

The study proposal in itself does not offer the solution of any problem, only the manner in which the solution will be approached. Study proposals usually begin by stating that a literature search will be made and the present state of the art determined. Then the design problems which are known to exist are named, and an attack on these problems is blocked out. The study proposal may name study team members and discuss their technical backgrounds. It may even specify that eminent specialists will be hired for consultation.

Study proposals are often the forerunners of valuable new hardware programs, and thus are contested far more than their small funding would seem to merit. Indeed, in a hot competition, interested bidders may attack and solve fundamental problems even in the study proposal, expending their own money to get a headstart on the competition.

The final study awards may go to one or to two or more of the competitors. In the latter case, competition will continue through the study and into the development phase. When the study is purely analytical, as many university studies are, the competition is more restricted, and, indeed, may involve only one invited bidder. The study itself must be considered an investigation report, a type of report to be described in 10.5.2.

10.2.2   Development Proposals

The award of a study contract does not necessarily win a corporation or institute the development contract. After the final studies have been received, a request for bids on a development proposal will be prepared and sent to qualified institutions and corporations. The list of interested bidders in this case will necessarily be smaller than the list for a study proposal, because far more research, testing, and manufacturing facilities will be required to support the contract. Indeed, at this stage, several companies may desire to bid as one team, pooling their resources.

The new request for proposal usually will direct that the study results of the previous round of bidding be implemented wholly or in part, thus giving the group which won that competition some advantage. The new request will also ask for separate manufacturing schedules and cost estimates. The development proposal itself is a technical report describing how the bidder proposes to go about designing, building, and testing a small number of developmental models of the system. (A limited example was given in 9.3.4.) The outline for a large development proposal is given below. It could outline, for instance, the development of a new missile flight control system.

DEVELOPMENT PROPOSAL OUTLINE

1. System Performance Requirements (from bid request)
2. System Operating Modes
3. Description of Proposed Configuration
   3.1 Mechanical Components
   3.2 Sensing Elements
   3.3 Computing Elements
   3.4 Control Elements
   3.5 Adaptability for Future Requirements
4. Design Principles
   4.1 Mechanical Design
   4.2 Logical Design
   4.3 Electronic Design
   4.4 Power Design
   4.5 Packaging Design
5. Reliability and Qualification Testing
6. Flight Test

This development proposal begins by restating requirements given in the proposal bid request, then enlarging on them. When several companies are members of the proposal team, each may contribute a section. For instance, one company might bid on the missile radar, one on the computer, one on the flight control system, and one on the rocket elements. The proposal team leader might bid on the airframe and on the test program management. The proposal team leader, in this case, is responsible for getting out the proposals, including the management proposal (which will be described) and the cost proposal (not a technical report).

10.2.3   Management Proposals

The management proposal is usually submitted later than the equipment development proposal, because it must be based on that proposal. The management proposal, or report, deals primarily with the management team and with the company facilities available to support the technical development. It usually describes key management personnel and their experience in appropriate fields, outlines the corporate facilities for large-scale production and testing, and reviews corporate practices which will be followed to insure product quality, reliability, ease of maintenance, and standardization of components. Here is a brief phrase outline for such a report.

MANAGEMENT PROPOSAL OUTLINE

1. Corporate and team organization charts
2. Background of key personnel
3. Corporate and team experience in field
4. Quality control and reliability practices
5. Engineering, manufacturing, and test facilities
6. Development and test schedules

The management proposal at this stage does not necessarily reflect production capabilities, because a production contract is not proposed at this time. Only development manufacturing of a few engineering models is pertinent. However, design which will permit ease of production later on is important. All such considerations, as a matter of fact, can be gathered into a list of rather ugly-sounding words: producibility, maintainability, operability, reliability, functionability, and flexibility (or changeability).

Once a development and test program has been successfully completed, the corporate team is usually given a follow-on production contract. The follow-on program, which arises naturally out of the development program, usually is not subject to the fierce competition of the earlier proposals. The production proposal itself will deal with technical plans, management, and costs, with the costs becoming much more important and the technical plans filling less space in the proposal.

10.3   **PROGRAM PLANNING DOCUMENTS**

Once a production contract has been awarded (or even earlier with large-scale development contracts), the technical reporting enters the program planning stage. In this stage, various technical planning documents are written, among which are facilities plans,

166

test plans, manufacturing plans, maintenance plans, support plans, training plans, reliability and quality control plans, configuration control plans, and over-all or summary plans.

Some of these documents can be quite large, running up to several volumes and a thousand or more pages. Furthermore, they are all subject to frequent updating, perhaps monthly, quarterly, or yearly. They are probably most widely used during the early stages of a program when no hardware exists, and the vital concern necessarily is with paperwork. At this time, also, key program changes can occur, requiring drastic revision of plans.

When equipment has been designed and manufactured, the planning documents become historical records, except for the latest documents in the cycle, such as test plans, training plans, maintenance plans, and support plans.

10.3.1   Program Summary Plan

The program summary plan may be viewed as a lengthy amplification of both the original technical proposal and the management proposal. Here is a sample outline:

PROGRAM SUMMARY PLAN OUTLINE

1. Management Plan
    1.1   Management Organization Chart
    1.2   Planning Control
    1.3   Cost Control
    1.4   Manpower Control
    1.5   Design and Change Control
    1.6   Subcontractor Control
    1.7   Contract Administration
    1.8   Equipment Production Control
    1.9   Program Schedule Control
2. Technical Development Plan
    2.1   Technical Requirements Analysis
    2.2   Equipment Analysis
    2.3   Development Engineering
    2.4   Operating Systems Technology
    2.5   Ground Service Equipment
    2.6   Test Sequence Logic
3. Operations Plans
    3.1   Facilities Plan
    3.2   Manufacturing Plan
    3.3   Quality Assurance Plan

3.4   Test Plan
3.5   Logistics Support Plan

The program summary plan, an over-all document, gives a bird's-eye view of the program better than any other document. Many of its sections are amplified in subsidiary, detailed operating plans, which are described next.

10.3.2   Facilities Plan; Manufacturing Plan

The facilities plan describes buildings, equipment, and test areas and works out requirements for additional facilities to be built or leased, if these are needed. This plan considers manufacturing, office, and service space, as well as applied-science laboratories, computer simulation capabilities, and medical and training equipment. It may also examine critically the facilities of subcontractors.

The manufacturing plan considers production schedules and controls (such as cost control, hours control, and design change control). It also sets tooling policy, subcontractor policy, manufacturing inspection policy, and shop training policy. Its central function, however, is to prescribe fabrication and assembly techniques for the equipment, as determined from drawings furnished by the engineering department. The manufacturing plan, finally, considers equipment handling, assembling, and checkout methods.

10.3.3   Test Plan

The test plans may be very lengthy documents, especially when large-scale tests are planned (such as orbital launches). The period for testing may be longer than any other period of the program. To certify a new space vehicle for manned use, for instance, requires as much testing over-all as has occurred in developing automobiles to their present state of reliability. Spacecraft testing for manned operations must, of course, be compressed in more intensive sequences. Still, certification can only be accomplished over time periods of years, involving costly, widespread teams of men and equipment.

Testing, furthermore, must occur at all levels of a hardware program. Early tests include circuit-element performance and reliability tests, breadboard design tests and functional tests, and

168

environmental tests of all kinds (usually including shock, sonic, vibration, humidity, salt-spray, moisture, fungus, contaminant, temperature, and pressure tests). Later tests include receiving, inspection, and acceptance tests, verification and integration tests, performance and qualification tests, flight tests, and so on.

As an indication of the contents of test plans, here is an outline for a typical large-scale flight test plan:

SPACECRAFT FLIGHT TEST PLAN OUTLINE

1. Introduction
2. Test Objectives and System Priorities
3. Mission Description
4. Description of Test Vehicle
5. Structural Design Criteria
6. Aerodynamic Stability
7. Instrumentation Requirements
8. Tracking and Support Data Requirements
9. Test Management Organization
10. Prelaunch Operations
11. Pad and Range Safety Requirements
12. Recovery Requirements
13. Data Reduction and Test Reporting
14. Ground Service Equipment Requirements

This test plan, when filled out, might run to several hundred pages of description and analysis. Still, it is only a plan and not a procedure. Test procedures, including a countdown procedure, must be written later, detailing every operational step performed by every man in the test. (Procedures will be discussed in 10.8.)

10.3.4   Other Program Plans

Other program plans are the maintenance plan, logistics support plan, training plan, quality plan, reliability plan, and configuration control plan. Each of these technical reports can be the subject of thousands of hours of labor.

The maintenance plan is a document detailing plans to maintain all operating and servicing equipment in good order throughout the months of the program. This equipment might include tracking networks, computer centers, cryogenic facilities, dust-free laboratory and work areas, and special laboratories, in addition to ordinary development, manufacturing, and test facilities. Types of maintenance functions are inspection, servicing, adjustment, calibration, modification, repair, transportation, and overhaul.

The logistics support plan details all program support services, such as laboratory and photographic services, security guards, reproduction and printing, technical illustrating, publishing, and library support. The employment of many technical writers is usually called out in this support plan.

The training plan outlines on-the-job training courses and schedules for a large assortment of personnel who will be performing newly established functions—from specialty-welders to astronauts. A group of astronauts pictured in the Sunday pictorial section of the newspaper, for instance, perhaps engaged in climbing over lava beds in Hawaii or hacking a path through some jungle, is evidence of the operation of a widespread training plan. The training plan also covers design and manufacture of training aids and training handbooks. Even university courses may be offered to engineers specializing in new and complicated fields, such as rocket propulsion, cryogenics, and spacecraft tracking.

The configuration control plan outlines, largely in sketches and charts, the exact equipment conformation (or mated configuration) associated with each stage of development, manufacture, and test. This plan typically pictures a series of equipment building-blocks, each series increasing in complexity until a complete configuration for test or delivery is established.

The quality assurance plan outlines a series of manufacturing inspections and checks, usually performed by a special test group whose purpose it is to insure that the requisite quality is being built into the hardware. The quality assurance plan can also provide initial design checks to insure that integrity and reliability are implicit in the design. This sort of integrity is provided by high-performance components, paralleling of functions, fail-safe design, and overdesign for the particular job. The quality assurance plan thus is a technical report describing the manner in which all these checks will be provided. The phrase *quality assurance* is not always defined alike by different organizations. Sometimes it includes the reliability functions.

Reliability in experimental equipment design means the analysis and testing associated with the establishment of a reliability index. This index might give the probability of successful performance for a given vehicle or component on a particular mission. All test results associated in any manner with the equipment and all performance and failure results are used in establishing the reliability index. Usually, equipment is not considered to be mission-qualified, or man-rated, perhaps, until the reliability index has exceeded a certain value. Successful testing and successful performance act to increase this reliability measure, but failures and nonperformance of any sort decrease it. The reliability plan in its broadest sense, then, is a technical report outlining the analytical and procedural approach necessary for establishing a reliability index and, over a period of testing and usage, for increasing the index above the level required for qualification. Reliability analysis requires the use of advanced mathematical techniques. This is especially true for experimental equipment.

10.4   SPECIFICATIONS

The writing of engineering specifications requires a knowledge of two specialized disciplines: engineering requirements and contractual performance requirements. Specifications are documents in which the law and engineering come together, and thus specifications should be legally phrased. They usually make difficult reading, and are not considered to be technical reports so much as contractual statements.

An equipment specification may be defined as an itemization of all the physical characteristics of the equipment in question. This will include such active capabilities as operating modes, display types and ranges, performance ranges, accuracies, power levels, and signal response characteristics. It also includes a listing of such passive parameters as weight, volume, configuration, packaging, power drain, and operating response in many different environments.

The following example displays typical specification language.

3.2.1.7.9.15 *Pitch Gimbal Position Indicator.* The pitch gimbal position needle indicator at $+8.0$ deg gimbal deviation shall deviate full scale in the positive sense (right deviation), and at -8.0 deg gimbal deviation it shall deviate full scale in the negative sense (left deviation). At zero deviation of the pitch gimbal, the needle indicator shall rest at the center of the scale (0 deg).

Another example is

> ... wiring shall be terminated at the bulkhead interface with a PT005E-26-6115E connector adapter at the interface. For interface configuration see para. 3.1.8.9.7 f (1) a.

Specifications are usually used only for reference; that is, as storehouses of numbers associated with the equipment. Thus, they should not be regarded as analytical or expository reports, and, for this reason, are usually written with little regard for ease of reading. Included in the many types of specifications are equipment, process, test, instrumentation, material, structural, and operating specifications.

10.5 INVESTIGATION REPORTS

Investigation reports include a wide range of general reports lying at the heart of the technical writing field. The most important of these include test reports, experimental investigation reports, data reports, and study reports.

10.5.1 Test Reports

The final test report for a large-scale test, such as the Mercury and Gemini series of manned orbital space flights, can be an important historical document. The following outline is suitable for such a test report, but it is also suitable for reports on small-scale tests.

GENERAL TEST REPORT OUTLINE

1. Summary of Test Results
2. Introduction to Test Mission
3. Test Objectives
4. Test Configuration
5. Pretest Preparation
6. Test Performance
7. Test Evaluation
8. Problem Summary
9. References

10.5.2 Experimental Investigation Reports

The typical experimental investigation report usually involves an induction-deduction sequence of some sort. Readers of engi-

172

neering journals, such as the *IEEE Transactions* and the *AIAA Journal*, are familiar with this type of learned report, an outline for which follows:

EXPERIMENTAL INVESTIGATION REPORT OUTLINE

1. Abstract
2. Introduction (includes purpose, previous work in field)
3. Equations Governing Experimental Phenomena
4. Experimental Test Equipment
5. Experimental Data Analysis
6. Comparison With Theory
7. Conclusions
8. Acknowledgments
9. References

Note that this outline for an engineering paper or report is longer than those presented in Chapter 12 for scientific papers. The engineer usually has more space than the scientist.

Publication in any type of journal requires special mention of other workers when any of their results happen to pertain to the experiment. This time-honored courtesy, which one scientist offers others in the field, is reminiscent of the round of introductions which occur at a formal dinner before the serious business of eating can be concluded. All the earlier workers in the field must be listed in "References" in terms of their pertinent published papers, while associates and contributors to the experiment reported are thanked in "Acknowledgments." The author of the paper should also learn and use such footnote-French as *ibid.*, *loc. cit.*, *op. cit.*, and *et al.* All the pleasant amenities which grace scientific dialogue are described specifically in style guides.

The familiar laboratory report is an informal example of an experimental investigation report. Usually such a memorandum, or memo report, describes a small-scale investigation which is written up for internal distribution only. It might omit items 1, 2, 8, and 9 of the outline.

10.5.3 Data Reports

Engineering data reports do not offer scope for standard technical writing beyond, perhaps, a thin summary, introduction, and conclusion. These reports may include lists of equipment and parts, tables of measurement descriptions and instrumentation requirements, sets of engineering formulas and scale factors, computer programming tables, and sets of operating parameters. Many of these lists and tables are coded line by line in a computer memory, where they are updated or corrected as required. New entries, deletions, and corrections are accomplished simply by writing out the new line, punching a computer entry card, and inserting this information into the computer memory. The computer will automatically make space for new material, renumber lists, sequences, and pages as required, and close up and rearrange as instructed. When a new report is to be published, it will type out a fresh, perfect set of master sheets on command.

Here is a sample line of this type:

Meas	Id	Descrip	Signal Range Low	High	Accu-racy	Signal Cond
GRS 8490 SM		ENGINE 1 FIRED	OPEN	CLOSE	NONE	CC1 80 1

The information coded in this line is extensive. The processing of an automatic measurement made aboard a space vehicle module (SM) is described. The measurement is identified explicitly, its descriptive display label is given, and signal range (usually in volts), signal accuracy, and signal conditioning or processing are described. The signal in this example has only two discrete values (OPEN, CLOSE).

This sort of automation can relieve the typist, proofreader, and technical editor of their drabbest duties, leaving them free to work with text.

10.5.4   Study Reports

Study reports are usually mathematical reports, written to break new ground in some research or advanced engineering topic. The entire field of trajectory analysis, for instance, is mathematical, and guidance and navigation topics require abstruse analysis before any useful equipment can be designed.

Computer simulation is a form of particular problem analysis which is highly useful when the general mathematical analysis is too formidable to be carried through. Reentry of a piloted spacecraft into the earth's atmosphere, for instance, can be simulated, or modelled, on a computer. Particular spacecraft responses to

174

particular pilot control patterns can be conveniently plotted as a result of the study. Here is a possible outline for such a study:

STUDY REPORT OUTLINE

1. Summary of Study Results
2. Introduction to Study Problem
3. Symbols and Nomenclature
4. Simulation Configuration Equations
   4.1 Model of Spacecraft
   4.2 Model of Atmosphere
   4.3 Computer Programming
   4.4 Pilot Controls and Displays
5. Simulation Results
6. Conclusions and Recommendations
Appendix A. Equations of Spacecraft Motion
Appendix B. Data Tables and Curves
References

10.6 QUALITY CONTROL AND RELIABILITY REPORTS

10.6.1 Quality Control Reports

Quality control reports do not present as large a scope for expository writing as test reports and investigation reports. Several small periodic reports may be included under this heading, such as acceptance-test reports, inspection reports, sampling reports, qualification reports, and status reports. Acceptance tests are performed when equipment is purchased from a supplier or subcontractor and accepted by the contractor. Qualification tests are performed to certify that equipment is qualified for use in certain critical ways, such as flight test. A quality status report may be issued from time to time describing the level of certification of all equipment components on a critical program.

The final predelivery test of a major system is called an end-item test, and report of this test will be made in the final quality control report. On successful completion of this test, the equipment will be delivered together with an acceptance data package supplied by the contractor. This data package consists of many reports, including specifications, drawings, a historical report, transportation, handling, and storage procedures, description manuals, and quality control and reliability reports.

Program Documentation Requirements 175

10.6.2 Reliability Reports

Reliability planning reports for a program have already been described (10.3.4). The reliability assessment of a system must be continually updated by information received in small, periodic reports, including failure reports and analyses, off-limits tests, and sampling tests. In addition, all test results and equipment operating times must be reported in such a manner that they can be used in the reliability assessment. The updated reliability analysis is issued from time to time in a reliability status report.

10.7   PROGRESS REPORTS

Information about the progress and present status of a long research or development program is usually passed to the customer in periodic progress reports. Progress reports are comprehensive and expository and offer large scope for the technical writer. In the early and middle stages of a program, they are particularly important, because they are the only "hardware" the customer sees, but in later stages they may not be as important as the test report and data report.

Some progress reports go to the customer as letters, some as monthly summaries, and some as extended quarterly reports. Progress in program development may be reported in various ways. It can be reported in terms of official milestones reached and passed (significant tests successfully performed, designs formalized and released, and test models delivered). It can also be reported as percentage of completion of various research, design, and fabrication sequences. A status graph or bar chart can show, for instance, the design percentage of completion for the major components of a doppler radar, as "transmitter design 50% complete," "antenna design 25% complete," and "power supply design completed and released."

A large progress report must include sections written by persons in all areas of the program. It will be the task of some technical editor to assemble these contributions and prepare a uniformly written and comprehensive rough draft. He then must arrange for typing, review, reproduction, and distribution. A full quarterly report of this type can run to a hundred pages, including status charts, photographs of equipment under development, block dia-

176

grams, and any significant new analyses which have been performed. Technical advances of any sort should be reported in this document for quick dissemination. These advances might pertain to new materials, new circuits, and new theory.

The outline for a large progress report generally begins with a program description and review of previous work reported.

PROGRESS REPORT OUTLINE

1. Abstract of Current Status
2. Description of Contract Requirements
3. Component Breakdown and Description
4. Summary of Past Work
5. Progress During Report Period
6. Plans for Next Report Period
7. Technical Advancements
8. Bibliography

The most significant item in this list of headings is item 5, which describes actual progress during the period of interest. Some of the other sections can be regarded as boilerplate material, changing only slightly each report period. In a smaller progress letter, items 2, 3, 6, 7, and 8 might be deleted entirely.

10.8   PROCEDURES

Procedures resemble specifications in being shaped strongly by requirements other than those for good expository writing. A typical procedure consists almost entirely of numbered consecutive commands for the operation of complex equipment. Countdowns for the purpose of launching an intercontinental missile, for instance, are one publicized example. A long procedure can require tremendous skill and effort in the preparation, and may run to several hundred pages of minutely detailed steps extending in time over two or three days. The excellence of such a procedure is judged almost entirely by engineering standards, however. Writing the rigidly controlled commands does not require the exercise of a large vocabulary or clever syntax, as will appear in the part of an imaginary procedural sequence which is given. The sequence might be used to check out a spacecraft attitude control system before launch.

Program Documentation Requirements   177

Sequence Number	Command Station	Check-out Station	Command
16-019	STC	CCL	Panel 16. Position BGP POWER sw. to ON.
16-020	STC	CCL	Panel 16. Position ΔV ACCEL sw. to ON.
16-021	STC	CCR	Panel 18. a. Position AC INV BUS 1 to φ A. b. Verify AC VOLTS reads less than 90 VAC. c. Position AC INV BUS 1 to φ B. d. Verify AC VOLTS reads less than 90 VAC.
16-022	STC	SCS	Console 90. Start B/G REC by depressing 200 MM/SEC sw.
16-023	STC	SCS	Record range time _____ .

There are many types of procedures. A list might include test procedures, checkout procedures, process control procedures, transportation, handling, and storage procedures, inspection procedures, operations procedures, and maintenance and repair procedures. These are important documents, requiring the skills of many engineers and technical writers in the preparation. Many such procedures are now prepared by electronic data processing techniques, using numbers to code entire commands. Such coding is not difficult to learn, and it simplifies greatly the actual labor of writing, correcting, and updating. The technical writer who learns these data processing skills will find his value to his organization greatly enhanced.

10.9   HANDBOOKS AND MANUALS

The two terms *handbook* and *manual* have been used in different senses in the industry. A manual, probably a more general term, describes technical processes and equipment in such a manner as to explain the theory of operation and also furnish detailed operating steps. Handbooks are usually more restricted in scope, being small, convenient, rugged reference (rather than explanatory) documents which can be opened and used on the job under trying conditions.

The writing of a large manual is one of the triumphs of the profession. The writer or editor of such a document must exercise every possible skill of his ingenious profession. This array of skills includes knowledge as an engineer and draftsman, considerable writing ability, familiarity with the processing of illustrations, photographs, and blueprints, knowledge of all the ingenuities of report printing and reproduction, acquaintance with library research procedures and company work procedures, intimacy with NASA and military specifications, and the ability to deal pleasantly with people at many work levels. The manual under preparation may require a year in work and run to several hundred pages of highly accurate, highly varied, and highly complex material. The text will require expository, descriptive, and analytic writing skills, and may be read by persons of every educational level from tenth grade to Ph. D.

The manual form can accommodate itself to varying requirements ranging from a strictly procedural type of document—"Do this, do this, do this, etc."—to a modified textbook in which GI's and second-class seamen, perhaps, can be instructed in some of the subtleties of the bewildering technical world they inhabit.

The military and government specifications regulating the format and content of manuals and handbooks constitute in themselves as remote an area of knowledge to most people as chamber music of the seventeenth century. The manual writer, as a consequence of his intense specialization, tends to be an independent and highly paid worker. Many skilled manual writers travel, like fruit workers, from orchard to orchard across the country as the plums of overtime work come into season in different sections of the aerospace industry. Living in well-appointed trailers, migrating between Florida, Phoenix, Los Angeles, Seattle, and Long Island as the season favors, these wandering writers enjoy a colorful existence.

In the sample outline for a manual which is given, subheadings are furnished to accommodate the many pages of text.

RADAR MANUAL OUTLINE
1. Introduction (purpose, arrangement of manual, limitations, changes)
2. Radar Set Description
   2.1   Radar Operational Capabilities
   2.2   Major Functions and Components

2.3   Component Description
2.4   Operating Modes and Parameters
2.5   Controls and Displays
3. Shipment and Installation
3.1   Crating for Shipping
3.2   Transportation and Handling
3.3   Uncrating and Installation
3.4   Installation Checkout
4. Radar Set Test Equipment
4.1   Test Equipment Supplied
4.2   Special Tools
4.3   Test Equipment Required But Not Supplied
5. Theory of Operation
5.1   Component Signal Flow Diagrams
5.2   System Integrated Flow Diagrams
5.3   Operating Mode Analysis
6. Checkout and Repair
6.1   Checkout
6.2   Maintenance Routines
6.3   Calibration and Alignment
6.4   Troubleshooting and Repair
7. Subsystem Analysis
7.1   Operating Procedures
7.2   Sketches and Photographs
7.3   Wiring Diagrams
8. Subsystem Schematics
9. Index

11 Technical Publications Organization

11.1 PUBLICATIONS DEPARTMENT

11.1.1 Survey of Technical Report Functions

An organization must exist to publish all the funded reports which were described in Chapter 10. This organization is usually a part of the corporate structure of the research and development contractor. Publications work can be subcontracted, but this practice is not often followed. The engineers and scientists who perform the studies and development work are, by all odds, most capable of writing the funded reports, and, in one way or another, this writing task usually falls, section by section, on their patient shoulders. Some of these engineers are, fortunately, capable writers; others find writing distasteful and give the task only perfunctory attention. The result, especially with large documents, can be a patchy, sometimes illegible, rough draft, handwritten or typed in its various sections, cut, pasted, stapled, and clipped haphazardly, perhaps misspelled, poorly illustrated, and uneven in style and format.

It is the function of the contractor's publications department (that is, of some technical editor) to receive the rough draft, inevitably late in delivery, and make order of its disorder. In the remaining time, the technical editor must perform the thousand tasks leading to publication and delivery. These tasks seem chaotic, but they can be grouped in a roughly sequential set of functions as follows:

1. Schedule key dates well ahead of time, such as delivery of rough draft sections, delivery for review and approval, delivery for printing. These dates should be published in a letter to all concerned.

2. Obtain work approvals and charge accounts for all who require them, such as artists, typists, and printers.

3. Interview engineers who are responsible for section writing, and, insofar as possible, prescribe a uniform style and format. The style and format should be determined with reference to the company style guide. In many cases, report form and text are based on the form and text of a previous report. In this case, the editor should supply the writer with his section of the previous report. Often the new section can be obtained by "red-lining" the former section. Such red-lining saves immensely on writing, makeup, review, and typing time.

4. Aid in the preparation and reproduction of rough draft material. The engineering writer, even in the largest organization, often has poor typing support and inadequate knowledge of reproduction processes. The specialized knowledge of the technical editor can be useful in this regard.

5. Collect finished rough drafts, hopefully on schedule, and edit them for uniformity. The technical editor must, at this point, satisfy himself that he understands the report completely in a "reading" sense. He is not responsible for technical content, but he must be prepared to answer all questions which a typist, an artist, or his own supervisor might ask about the content. This understanding inevitably requires discussion with the engineering writer to clear up inconsistencies, misstatements, garbled information, and extraneous comments.

6. Parcel out report work to typists, technical artists, and possibly to a style editor (or policy editor). Some publications departments employ style editors to perform editing in accordance with a style manual.

7. Secure engineering approval of any text and illustration changes deemed necessary.

8. Reproduce perhaps five review copies (after typing and illustrating work is done) and distribute these for engineering review.

9. Obtain engineering approvals; incorporate engineering corrections and changes in the master copy; also obtain a patent office review and security classification review, if necessary. The reviewers might include, in sequence, the originating en-

gineer, the engineering supervisor, the chief engineer, and the program manager or perhaps a vice president.

10. Arrange for report printing and distribution. (The report distribution list is often prepared by the technical editor.)

11.1.2 Other Publications Functions

This survey of publishing functions is based on the largest possible view of the work which might be assigned to a technical editor. The editor's job description may assign him much less scope in a large organization. The handbook or manual writer, on the other hand, may have a different job description. Since he is an engineering writer and editor both, he has complete responsibility for the production of his document. A brochure writer must also function both as writer and editor.

The publications department must be set up to support all the listed functions and, in many cases, allied functions as well. Allied documents to be edited and published might include the following:

1. Training and educational material
2. Product-line brochures
3. Trade and technical symposium display and handout copy
4. Briefing posters and slides
5. Papers for submission to learned journals
6. Speech and trade magazine copy
7. Film and TV scripts

The totality of functions of a large publications department can be assigned to four or five separate groups. These might include the manuals group, technical reports group, proposals group, report production group, and promotional copy group, as shown in the organization chart on page 184.

11.1.3 Technical Reports Group

The technical editors are usually gathered into one group called, variously, "Technical Reports," "Engineering Reports," or "Report Editing." Such groups may range from two or three up to perhaps thirty professional editors and writers. These people will have varied educational backgrounds, including journalism, English literature, engineering and physics, education, business administration, and mathematics. Most will have a bachelor of arts or bachelor of science degree, but some will have a master's degree.

Technical Publications Organization 183

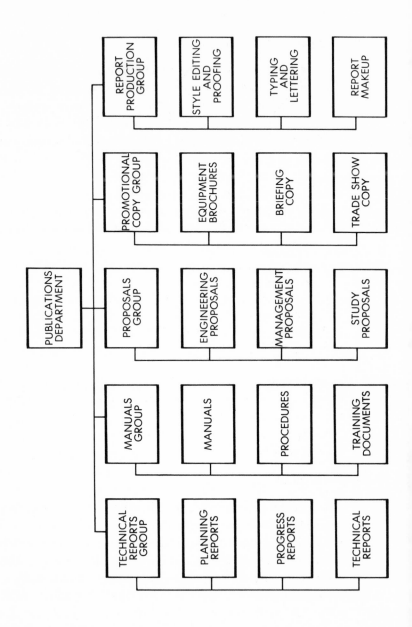

184

A large group of editors may be subdivided further into units concerned with the preparation of such documents as technical reports and planning reports. Furthermore, many technical editors will become proficient in a technical specialty, such as autonavigators or radars, and be assigned work in their special field only.

The technical editor is charged with working a rough draft into the format prescribed by the corporation style guide, and this function, together with report coordination, will occupy most of his time. Style editing usually includes editing the manuscript for proper punctuation, grammar, spelling, headings, paging, and the like, and proper setup of tables and illustrations. It can also include the makeup of lists of symbols, references, nomenclature, and abbreviations, and the writing of the foreword, table of contents, list of illustrations, list of tables, table and illustration titles, the abstract, and often the summary or introduction. Finally, the editor must give instructions for setup to the typist and technical illustrator and proofread the material these people return to him.

11.1.4   Use of Style Guides

A thorough knowledge of the institutional style guide is required for the performance of style editing. Style guides, it can be repeated, do not deal with style in the general sense discussed in section 2.4. Rather, they are a collection of local or house rules for treating the mechanical details of page organization and makeup.

The most widely used general style manual for expository writing is the *United States Government Printing Office Style Manual*. This compendious work is the model for many thinner style guides, but it does not deal with scientific and technical writing style specifically. Hence, the reader will search there in vain for the solution to many problems of technical nomenclature, hyphenation, abbreviation, etc. Nevertheless, this manual's authority, reputation, low cost, and availability (write to Superintendent of Documents, Washington, D.C.) make it a bargain. There are useful sections in it, for instance, on spelling, punctuation, abbreviation, compounding, and use of numerals, symbols, and tables in text.

There are many less useful but more curiously interesting sections of the *GPO Style Manual*. One gives the county names for each state and another the botanical names of common plants. The reader may learn, for example, that the apostrophe is omitted in plant names with a possessive element, as in *babysbreath* and *devils-paintbrush*. He may learn that "Peru" in *apple-of-Peru* retains its capital letter. He may also learn that letters illustrating shape and form are properly set in gothic capitals, as *U-shape*, *T-bone*, *I-beam*, and *A-frame*.

The *GPO Style Manual* also contains useful instructions on page makeup for printing. In reading these instructions, the student encounters a cast of characters who might well have graced a Dickens novel. The *Public Printer*, the *Chief Copy Preparer*, and the *Chief Reviser* are among the capitalized and periwigged aristocracy, while a legion of lowercase types such as *copy preparers* and *press revisers* scurry about among the ink pots and paper stacks. An occasional lord of the realm is also announced, coming in to have his punctuation and capitalization adjusted, such as the *British Consul*, the *Chief Magistrate*, and *Your Excellency*. Each of these personages will model some comma or trick of capitalization or hyphenation with a pomp and dignity unknown in purely scientific and technical writing.

Institutional style guides, in comparison, offer much poorer reading, and are, taken altogether, a rather quarrelsome lot. A careful reading of half a dozen can reveal many contradictory requirements. There is no uniform rule from one style guide to the next, for instance, regarding placement of a comma before the *and* preceding the last item of a series. Heading makeup is not standardized either, nor is the meaning of *foreword* and *preface*, nor, for that matter, are the capitalization and spelling of *Fiber glas(?)*, *fiberglass(?)*, *fiberglas(?)*. The recommended use of numerals in text can also differ widely (whether to write 15 or *fifteen*, for instance).

It is unfortunate that the practicing technical writer who changes jobs must also change style guides. This requirement may occur even when he changes from one division of a company to another, or when his supervisor alone changes. A new supervisor or chief may consider it his first duty to sweep out old, onerous style practices and institute new, onerous ones. He may, for instance, absolutely forbid the use of some innocuous phrase such as *due to* or *in order that* (if he has been promoted from the technical illustration area of the publications department). Then, having settled the matter of good style, the new supervisor may turn his attention to the matter of those employees who have been arriving five minutes late at their desks because the employee parking lot is not large enough to accommodate everyone.

Amid the present welter of confusing style guide requirements, there are a few encouraging prospects. One is the increasing authority of a few conscientious style guides devoted explicitly to scientific and technical writing. These style guides include the American Institute of Physics *Style Manual* and the American Standards Association publication *American Standards for Drawings, Symbols, and Abbreviations.*

Many NASA and Department of Defense funded reports, particularly manuals and handbooks, must follow style specifications set forth by the contracting agency. These specifications are necessary for such lengthy, specialized reports, but they are not necessarily suited to accommodate the requirements of general expository writing.

11.1.5   Typing and Illustrations Groups

11.1.5.1   TYPING GROUP

The typing group will be discussed here to the extent that their work relates to the technical editor's function. When a technical editor plans his dummy pages, he usually finds three distinct types of material to be dealt with. These include (1) report text in paragraph form, (2) special display material, including tables and formulas, and (3) illustrations (including diagrams, photographs, sketches, and curves).

The first item requires that the editor obtain the services of a standard reproduction typist, who will reproduce his text as fresh master copy on heavy reproduction stock. The reproduction typist is trained in the use of her electric typewriter and in the placement of copy, headings, and page number on the formal report paper. This stock usually comes provided with institution name and symbol printed at the top and with many typing guide lines printed in a light-blue photoinsensitive shade. (These guide lines disappear when the report master page is photo-reproduced.)

Technical Publications Organization   187

The reproduction typist usually does not have on her keyboard the many symbols and special characters needed for an analytical report. Therefore, she must leave blank spaces in the text where these appear. A special typist, sometimes called a varitypist, must insert the symbols and formulas. Her special typewriter will possess an entire catalog of fonts, or sets of type faces, any of which can be inserted in the machine. The report will not be completely typed, then, until both typists have entered their material. Furthermore, any tables which require lining, or boxing, usually must be delivered to the illustrations department for this purpose, along with all the other art work.

11.1.5.2 ILLUSTRATIONS GROUP

In formal reports, all illustrations work is prepared by professional illustrators. Photographs, to reproduce well in offset printing, must be airbrushed, or otherwise treated, to bring out significant detail and also to remove unwanted and confusing detail. Usually a halftone print is made of the airbrushed photograph, after which an offset printing plate can be made.

The technical illustrator usually makes each sketch or diagram in some convenient size on a separate piece of vellum paper. He may hand-letter the vellum, using various mechanical printing aids, or he may use ready-printed lettering, symbols, and shading which he simply pastes in place on the vellum. This art work is then marked for photo-reproduction in the size desired for mounting in the blank space left on the report master page. The lines and lettering should, of course, be sized originally in such a manner that they come out in proper dimensions after being amplified or reduced by the photographic process.

Photographic halftones are usually not mounted on the master page with textual material before the printing plates are made. Printing plates for all halftone material are made separately, using special film adapted for getting the high contrast needed for good photographic reproduction. The master printing plates are then made up as units for the actual printing run.

It can be remarked here that some technical illustrators are notoriously poor spellers. Indeed, they are often indifferent to spelling, being concerned with more weighty topics such as perspective, shading, and projection. Under these circumstances, the technical editor is advised to proofread his art work carefully. It is conceivable that the artist who renders a correct perspective view of the entire lower equipment bay of a bomber will misspell some simple statement, such as "Flashing red light indicates power on."

11.1.6   Reproduction and Printing Services

11.1.6.1   ELECTROSTATIC REPRODUCTION PROCESSES

Reproduction or duplication services may include copying by several modern processes. Those available to the technical writer often include the Ditto, Ozalid, and Xerox processes, and may include the Thermofax and Mimeograph processes (especially in smaller offices where a large service staff cannot be supported). Detailed knowledge of their physical principles is not needed to use these services. However, knowledge of the best master copy for each, and of flexibility, cost, timeliness, and quality of reproduction is useful.

The electrostatic type of machine (such as a Xerox or Bruning copier) accepts almost any type of master copy and gives a clear, permanent impression. (Light blue is the worst color to reproduce; standard Ditto copy, however, is purple enough to come through satisfactorily.) Electrostatic processes are costly and slow for large-volume work, but their quality, freedom from setup requirements, and flexibility usually make them favored for up to four or five quick, clean copies.

The copy for electrostatic reproduction can be patched together in many convenient ways, if necessary, without serious harm to the final appearance. Gummed strips can be mounted in place, cellophane tape emendations can be made, and white opaquing ink can be freely used to make typing corrections on the master copy or to obliterate fingerprints, coffee stains, and unwanted lines, words, and curlicues. Copy has even been stapled together for reproduction. That is, clipped-out Ditto paragraphs have been stapled in a sequence with printed or typed paragraphs, all on a common backing sheet, together with perhaps a sketch or two. When such master copy is reproduced it shows the staples and stray edge lines, but appears much neater, fresher, and more coherent than the master copy. Photographs can even be reproduced with reasonable clarity by this process if the machine operator takes care to obtain his best quality.

To a working editor who receives his rough draft in odd, scrambled bits and pieces, and is required to produce five quick review copies without typing support, electrostatic reproduction processes offer an eminently practical solution.   When more than perhaps four or five copies of his patchwork masterpiece are desired, it is probably wisest to print one electrostatic copy on vellum paper, then use this vellum as master copy for a process such as Ozalid (blueline or blackline).

11.1.6.2   AMMONIA VAPOR REPRODUCTION PROCESSES

Ammonia vapor reproduction processes such as Ozalid are advantageous when perhaps six to thirty medium-quality copies are required.   The chief requirement for the Ozalid master copy is that it appear on translucent material, such as vellum, or on a photographic transparency.   The Ozalid process itself requires the services of a trained operator, but it is quick and cheap, does not require much setup time, and is of good quality except where high resolution of detail is required.   The diazo dye in the reproduced lines tends to fade over a period of years, but this is not serious if the original impression is strong enough.   The ammonia vapor used in the process is a dry fixing agent for the diazo dye.

The technical editor who has worked with vellum master copy knows that it can be cranky and awkward at times, particularly when corrections must be made.   Since the copy must be translucent, any attempt to make changes on the fresh vellum tends to create smudges, blurs, and curlicues, which also appear on the reproduced copy.   Opaquing the vellum with white ink is impossible, of course, as are pasting and stapling of any sort.   Erasing inevitably tears the paper surface in small ways, tending to produce light smudges on the final copy.   Typing up new vellum inserts and stripping these into the master copy has been practiced with some success, but this introduces light edging lines on the final copy.   It must be concluded that, for the purposes of the technical editor who is charged with producing a few quick review copies of his material, ammonia vapor processes are not as flexible as electrostatic processes.

When the original master copy has been neatly typed on vellum, however, Ozalid reproductions can be rapidly and cheaply run, and, with their fresh ammonia odor, tend to wake up the reader who first receives them.

11.1.6.3 SPIRIT REPRODUCTION PROCESSES

The best known process of spirit reproduction is the Ditto process. The small, efficient Ditto machine is familiar to the average office worker, because it can be operated by relatively unskilled workers and is inexpensive and easily installed. The term *spirit* associated with this process refers to the chemical solution which the machine uses to wash the dye from the back of the Ditto master onto the reproduction copy.

The Ditto master copy is prepared by typing or drawing on a special master sheet with a heavily dyed backing sheet. The text and illustrations appear reversed, in heavy dye, on the back of the master sheet when the backing is removed. This master copy is then fixed on a drum which rotates and washes the spirit solution against the dye and onto the reproduction copy, picking up a fresh new sheet at each revolution.

Ditto is a very cheap and quick reproduction process, offering copy of relatively low quality suitable for interoffice work. The reproduced lines are usually clear, but coarse and unsuitable for curves, graphs, and detailed sketches. The number of good copies which can be reproduced is ordinarily limited to perhaps one hundred, except where special paper is used. Ditto and Ozalid cannot be considered true copiers, perhaps, because they do not copy everything. Xerox, on the other hand, is omnivorous, copying five-dollar bills equally with photographs of the technical editor's wife and his Friday paycheck.

11.1.6.4 PRINTING PROCESSES

The only printing process which will be discussed is photo-offset printing because it is used so universally for the final reproduction of high-quality technical reports. Offset printing machines require a large initial investment, longer setup time than other reproduction processes, and a crew of skilled operators. Nevertheless, for printings of thirty or more (or for printings of less than

Technical Publications Organization

thirty where high quality is desired), offset printing is the process of choice because of its low per-unit cost.

Photo-offset printing plates are usually prepared by photographing the report master pages and making page negatives which are used to prepare the printing plates. Once the plates have been prepared, they are mounted in automatic machines which turn out copies very quickly. The term *offset* applied to this process indicates that the printing plates are positive impressions of the master copy (rather than negative, or reversed, impressions, as with standard printing plates). The offset printing plates, after being inked, print a reversed impression on an offset roller which, in turn, reverses the copy to print positively on the report page. The offset roller thus gives the process its name.

In the multilith printing process, a simplified version of the photo-offset process, paper printing plates are prepared directly on a typewriter.

11.2 REPORT EDITING

11.2.1 Analyzing the Rough Draft

The technical editor who is assigned to edit and publish a lengthy technical document usually finds that his rough draft comes to him in a patchy, piecemeal state from several contributing engineering groups. This dishevelled appearance, however, should not lead him to scorn the technical content, which will have gone through careful engineering assessment and review. This sort of constant, agonized reappraisal, indeed, is usually what causes the patchwork appearance.

It is now the editor's task to prepare a final document in such good order—so pleasing to the eye and mind—that it will reflect all engineering care and scrupulosity. In practice, the editor can adopt either of two fundamentally different points of view toward this task. He can regard his job as a rather mechanical one in which he is called upon to fulfill certain stated forms with regard to punctuation, grammar, and surface appearance only. Or he can alter the expository text itself in an attempt to make good explanations out of possibly bad ones. Either point of view has its good points and bad points, as will be discussed.

The virtues of leaving the report content virtually unaltered—

the first course—are most apparent when the editor is unfamiliar with its content. This sort of discretion usually satisfies the engineering writer who cannot judge his own faults. It also saves editing time and review time by the engineering writer, who is pleased to note he has been judged a proficient writer. It may even avoid the insertion of editing mistakes.

The disadvantage of this easy treatment is that a large report often has sections contributed by genuinely poor writers, and some reworking of their text is in order. When these sections are carefully studied, a conscientious critic can usually detect many garbled, confused, and plainly contradictory statements. The writer of Section 3, for instance, may have updated his schedules, while the writer of Section 5 may have failed to do so. Or perhaps the new canard tail configuration may be discussed by the analysis group, but flight test still strings along with remarks about the abandoned tail configuration.

A trivial example of garbling can occur when a Xerox copier, perhaps, fails to reproduce the last line of an overtyped Ditto page. Any slight misadjustment of the copier can cause an important statement to be left off, and it is astonishing how far this garble can travel without detection.

Other common types of error in "multiman" reporting are the needless repetition of information from section to section, the lack of proper over-all introduction to major sections, great disproportion in the amount of detail from section to section, the lack of linking material, and nonuniform usage of tables, curves, and diagrams.

The editor who, alone, attempts to correct any of these errors is inviting trouble unless he knows explicitly what he is doing. He may mistake the sense of even simple, seemingly awkward statements unless he knows the jargon. On the other hand, a year's shrewd observation may acquaint an editor so well with the mental habits of "Homo Engineeriens" that he knows what the species is trying to say even before they—some few of them—missay it.

11.2.2   Obtaining Report Reviews

If the editor can demonstrate that a mistake has been made, his suggestions to the engineer will be valued. But if the engineer suspects that the argument is over some matter of "fancy words," he may suggest that the editor go to the chief engineer—or to some other place equally inaccessible.

Of course, the editor may simply make any changes in the copy he deems necessary and send it down the line for typing and eventual review in the hope that the changes will either (1) be unnoticed or (2) be noticed and praised. These hopes may be doomed to failure in either eventuality, life being what it is. In the long run, any error stands permanently, for all the world to discover, while any worthwhile change goes unnoticed and unsung. To paraphrase Mark Antony: "The evil that editors do lives after them; the good is oft interred with their bones."

The original writer of any section will give the edited copy by far its best review. It is up to the editor to give this person a simple, reasonable explanation for all changes he has made in the section. If he does this tactfully and straightforwardly, the review will be accomplished easily and other reviews will usually follow perfunctorily.

Sometimes a technical editor has to obtain the review of a style editor, or policy editor, in his own department. This person may make style-guide changes in the copy immediately before the typist gets it. This process, too, is fraught with danger. Sometimes a complicated technical explanation cannot be forced into the small, neat, and enamelled framework required by the style guide. For example, one style guide failed to list the definition for *psig*, or *pounds per square inch of gauge pressure*. The style editor, told not to use any undefined abbreviations, in order to promote reading clarity, determined from the guide that *psi* alone stood for *pounds per square inch*, and *g* alone stood for *gravity*. Then he virtuously wrote in *pounds per square inch of gravity* wherever *psig* appeared, which did nothing at all to aid the reader's comprehension.

11.2.3   Problems of Style

It is possible that a publications group can be supervised by a person who is not himself a good writer. Unfortunately, most people imagine instinctively that they are capable writers, and there is no easy way to prove that any of them are wrong. The judgment of writing, in this respect, resembles the judgment of humor.

194

The worst punsters and practical jokers imagine that they have the best sense of humor. The pompous writer imagines that a pompous style is best, and the hypocrite imagines that a woolly, secretive style is best. This sort of thing is most difficult to cope with in a supervisor. After all, didn't his pomposity, or hypocrisy, or whatever it was, get him into his present station? The fact that he is a cousin of the chief had nothing to do with it.

Under these circumstances, the good technical writer can adapt some sort of protective coloration: He can write in the ponderous, gray, and secretive style which characterizes many technical reports. Or he can continue to write clearly and openly, meanwhile suffering the penalties of being told his style is too obvious, or too unbusinesslike, or too undignified, or too immature.

It is unfortunate that these adjectives are sometimes used in judging technical writing. Fortunately, reading and writing tend, in the long run, to bore the kind of people who make such criticisms. The technical writer who offers no open quarrel with them can usually manage at last to write as he thinks best. His critics simply lose interest in the writing process. They prefer to play on people, not prose.

11.3   REPORT PROCESSING

11.3.1   Processing Survey

There are many rather mechanical processing functions which the technical editor should perform before he can be assured that the report will meet its delivery date. These processes include (1) preparing the report distribution list, (2) obtaining all signatures needed for report approval, (3) securing legal reviews and security reviews if necessary, (4) arranging for delivery of the typed and illustrated master copy for printing, and (5) arranging for delivery of the collated, punched, and bound final copies to the customer.

It may happen that other offices, other personnel, are actually charged with performing these functions. Still, if some coordination is not provided, a report can dally along the way for a precious week while the customer wonders and growls. Typical examples of such dalliance can easily be found. In one case, a thick report was ordered to be stitched together at the printers. The stitching needles broke, in penetrating the bulky report, and new needles were ordered. The report was delayed needlessly in this way for eight days; punching and binding with staples or Acco fasteners would have been perfectly suitable, but no one was available to change the print-shop order.

In another case, a line was left off the report cover by the subcontractor, and a new printing was required by the purchasing agent. The missing line was trivial—not at all worth delaying the report six days. However, no one was available with the necessary perspective to make the assurances; thus, delay became inevitable.

11.3.2   Report Distribution List

Funded reports are distributed in a manner specified by the contract. Usually the contractor keeps as many reports as he needs for his internal distribution, and external distribution is made at the pleasure of the customer (or contracting agency). The total number of addressees may run to several hundred, and the distribution list may require continual revision. Sometimes the distribution list and the distribution function are controlled by the library staff. Sometimes a separate group, with a name such as "Reports Distribution," is charged with this function. In smaller institutions, the mailroom alone can handle distribution.

In any case, the technical editor of the report should be acquainted with the distribution list, its updating requirements, and report delivery requirements. Often the contract requires that several advance copies of the report be delivered quickly to the customer. For timely delivery of advance copies, it may be necessary to arrange beforehand for special wrapping and immediate air transportation of copies from the first printing run.

If reports are classified, or otherwise restricted, they may have to be hand-carried; that is, accompanied by a messenger whose duty it is to insure they are put in the hands of the addressee (for which the messenger will obtain a receipt). The bulk of other external reports can go by slower mail to research libraries and to allied contractors scattered throughout the nation. The distribution of internal reports is usually made by the library. The manner in which this group handles, classifies, indexes, abstracts, catalogs, and distributes new reports is discussed at length in

196

Chapter 13. In any case, the technical editor should be acquainted with all distribution requirements early in the report cycle; he should make whatever arrangements he is charged with before report printing.

11.3.3 Review and Approval Signatures

A report review form usually exists on which the names of those required by procedure to approve the report can be entered. The technical editor should fill out this form and submit it with review copies of the report. For all reports which obligate or commit the institution (such as proposals and specifications), it may be necessary to obtain approval signatures directly on the title page. This requirement is often followed for individually written research reports, too, and for certain internally distributed documents of smaller scope, such as procedures.

After an engineer has reviewed a document and entered his red-lined changes and corrections on the text, he usually signs the approval slip. After this, the review package is carried to the next reviewer without any intermediate retyping. The chief engineer or the program manager, however, may require fresh, entirely up-dated and corrected copy. In this case, the technical editor must return his marked-up review copy for the insertion of all changes on the master copy and for the printing of a fresh review copy. The master copy itself is not often submitted for review when there exists the possibility that changes will be entered on it. Such scribblings are difficult to remove and tend to degrade the appearance of the final printed copies.

The technical editor is usually the only person who can insure that all corrections have been faithfully entered. Report review at the higher levels is very perfunctorily accomplished, in most cases, and should not be depended upon to rectify errors which still exist.

11.3.4 Report Legal Review

Certain classes of reports (most often study reports, proposals, general specifications, and progress reports) require review by the institution's legal staff. This review is made to determine whether valuable proprietary information and patentable ideas have been discussed. There usually is a block on the report approval form requiring the signature of a legal officer to show that such a review has been made.

If information of this type does, in fact, appear in the report, the technical editor usually inserts a notice of patent application, or a notice of proprietary information, somewhere near the foreword. This insertion can be effected with a handstamp.

The patent application notice is a familiar one to most people. It usually states that a patent is pending for any patentable device described in the report. The proprietary information notice is not seen so often. It usually states something to the effect that information contained in the report is the property of the contractor, or of the U.S. Government, and that such information can only be used or revealed to others under terms of the secrecy agreement. This agreement will have been previously signed by all who qualify to receive the report.

The security classification of a report (such as *Secret* or *Confidential*) is assigned at the time the report is planned. Material should not be entered in the report, therefore, which is not in accordance with this classification. Special procedures for handling classified reports must also be followed. These special handling requirements fall in large degree on the broad shoulders of the technical editor.

11.3.5 Arranging for Printing

When a report has been approved and when all required corrections have been made by the illustrating and typing groups, the master pages must be delivered for printing. The print order form will specify the manner of printing, the number of copies, the date required, the manner of binding, and the type of cover.

For important reports, the cover usually must be designed and made up early to be ready at printing. Special bindings should also be ordered early. In a large institution, the bulk of printing and binding is accomplished internally. However, when the pressure of work is great, a job-shop printer may be selected to do the reproduction, collating, or binding.

198

The technical editor is rarely charged with mailing the report, but he should follow the mailing process. When time is important and a problem arises, it is useful to have someone on the spot who can judge the problem in its largest perspective. The technical editor, unquestionably, has this perspective. He is aware of technical content, schedule urgency, quality and security requirements, report priority, correction capabilities, and a dozen other factors. Thus, he can balance all claims made on the report by those who are processing it and arrive at a considered decision on what is most important: immediate delivery, for instance, or reprinting to get rid of some bad inkspots. To use a phrase common in engineering: he is the person most capable of making all trade-off decisions.

12 Scientific Papers and Theses

PROBLEMS OF SCIENTIFIC WRITING

The university scientist who writes a paper for a scholarly journal usually faces a trying set of problems. He may be writing, for instance, in his spare moments, not being given "company time" to produce his work on a fixed schedule. Furthermore, he may not have a professional publications worker at his elbow to take his coarse first draft and return him fresh, elegant copy for review. Nor does he have a fixed market for his copy—a funded report. Instead he must compete for space in the journals with eminent men in his field.

The university writer (or scientific writer, as he will be called) must be largely self-motivated, and he must fit rather onerous chores into his cramped schedule. Under these circumstances, his psychological distress may be more heartfelt than that of his counterpart in industry. The student in the university who must write a research thesis faces many of the problems that the faculty do, and the comments in this section must apply to the student writer's predicament also.

Many scientific writers, of course, turn out papers of excellent quality under the circumstances. Those papers that appear in the journals, however, do not give any measure of the hundreds that

200

are rejected, many of them because their worth is obscured by poor writing.

12.1.1 Verbal and Numerical Analysis

Many scientists prefer to analyze their experience in terms of geometrical and algebraic symbols rather than in terms of words. They have been rewarded for exercising their minds successfully in this manner all their college and professional lives, and so their natural preference is constantly reinforced. They may even state that making a scientist perform verbal analysis is as incongruous as asking a lawyer to perform vector analysis.

Perhaps much of the distaste for scientific writing comes because it is usually performed after the numerical analysis is accomplished and there is no emotional force left for the verbal analysis—none of the stimulus of curiosity, no expectation of a startling new insight, no thrill of invention. In this mood the researcher may be tempted to quote Hamlet: "How weary, stale, flat, and unprofitable seem to me all the uses of this world!" To admit the truth of these tendencies here, however, is not to banish them. They must somehow be contested by the scientific writer alone and resolute at his desk.

Scientists have sometimes enjoyed reporting their work. We may quote Sir Isaac Newton in evidence (from his "A New Theory of Light and Colors"):

> In the year 1666 . . . I procured me a triangular glass prism to try therewith the celebrated phenomena of colors. And . . . having darkened my chamber and made a small hole in my window-shuts, to let in a convenient quantity of the sun's light, I placed my prism . . . that it [the light] might thereby be refracted to the opposite wall. It was at first a very pleasing divertissement to view the vivid and intense colors produced thereby; but after a while applying myself to consider them more circumspectly, I became surprised to see them in an oblong form.

In this passage, Newton plainly enjoys remembering and describing his optics experiment. It may be worth noting that he used the personal pronoun *I* freely and did not hesitate to report his feelings. The modern scientist does not have such opportunities for pleasant self-expression and must write impersonally. This rule of impersonality was discussed in 4.1. It is another of the reasons why scientific writing has become such a chore.

12.1.2   Problems of Compression

The modern scientist may complain justly at this point that he would enjoy writing prettily too, but that the iron compression of sense demanded in his journals (as well as the rule of impersonality) precludes all such adornment. This fact cannot be denied. Most journals are published at a monetary loss and require subsidy. Their publication costs lie largely in their printing costs, and the number of printed pages must be severely limited. Therefore the scientist must be succinct. Indeed, the style guides of many journals state that economy of expression influences the acceptance of a paper.

It is unfortunate that long, complex sentences appear to be the chief result of many scientists' attempts to write succinctly. It is debatable whether long sentences, good or bad, do actually result in fewer words. It is plain enough that such sentences, however, often result in a loss of meaning.

The scientist who writes a long, difficult sentence can be compared to the supermarket shopper who returns home with many packages in the car and then tries to carry them all at once into the kitchen. Before he has finished with this plan, he may have spilled the potatoes over the lawn, crushed the bread, and disturbed the whole household with his shouts to open the kitchen door.

For example, here is a bewildering long sentence:

> The more precise techniques were discarded as being too expensive in time and effort in view of the complex chemistry of chondrites and the necessity, in these investigations, for data on the molecular weights of the species in the vapor and their accommodation coefficient in it not being readily available.

The meaning of this passage is not quite clear, because of overcomplex sentence structure and confused reference. The reference words in question are *these*, *their*, and *it*. A rewritten version follows:

> The more precise techniques were discarded as costing too much time and effort because of the complex chemistry of chondrites. A

202

precise technique would have required supplying the molecular weights of the species and their accommodation coefficients (which are not readily available) in the vapor.

Fewer words have been used in the second version, but this is not always possible in editing, because, to gain space, authors sometimes omit material which is necessary for clarity.

12.1.3   Caution in Writing

Another cramping requirement in scientific writing is the need for caution in statement. In explanatory writing, the reader, seeking to understand, normally allies himself with the writer in this attempt. Scientific writing, however, is usually argumentative writing in which the writer attempts to prove a contested point. Under these circumstances he is apt to regard his reader as critical. This reader may be seeking not to understand but to misunderstand if he is given the chance. Thus caution in statement is understandable. Such caution goes too far, however, when it withdraws into obscurity under the cover of many qualifying phrases and clauses. An example of this defect in style was given in 4.2.3. As indicated there, excessive caution usually results in cloudy, overlong statements.

12.1.4   Loss of Grammatical Coupling

Problems which beset the scientist in performing verbal analysis have been discussed, and some of the cramping restrictions he suffers with have been analyzed. It is suggested, in conclusion, that these restrictions, all more or less peculiar to scientific writing, tend to pyramid into one effect: the long sentence. These restrictions are (1) the rule of impersonality tending toward passive constructions, (2) the demand for economy of expression tending toward greater sentence content, and (3) the need for extreme caution tending toward obscure, highly qualified statement.

Successful reference and modification in a sentence depend strongly on nearness of the associated, or coupled, elements, as noun and pronoun, or noun and modifying clause. When sentence length and coupling distances increase, therefore, the grammatical associations become more tenuous, and often vanish entirely.

Scientific Papers and Theses   203

Other causes of the long sentence or loss of control of modification and reference have been discussed elsewhere; namely, writing with phrases (6.1.1), redundant writing (6.1.2), weak word choice (6.1.3), faulty modification (6.2.4), errors of number leading to errors of reference (6.3.2), and ambiguous reference (6.3.3). Aids to clarification of grammatical coupling include the standardization of terminology (9.3.5), the use of word repetition to link sentences and paragraphs (5.5.5), and the use of parallel phrasing (5.3). Understanding all these techniques is important if successful long sentences are to be written.

12.2   METHODS OF ORGANIZATION

12.2.1   Survey of Scientific Papers

A quick survey of scientific papers published in the journals should aid in classifying their types of organization. The scientific journals of interest include such eminent publications as *The Physical Review, Journal of the American Chemical Society, The Review of Scientific Instruments, Quarterly of Applied Mathematics, The Astrophysical Journal*, and *Nature*.

The unpracticed reader who opens some of these journals will be struck at once by the formidable and beautiful symbology of modern mathematics and science. The words and sentences appear at times as a sparse green foliage against the massive branching network of mathematical thought. Still, all equations are organized to be read cursively in the one-dimensional sense of sentences and paragraphs, and the principles of logical organization discussed in Chapters 7, 8, and 10 will apply. (See, in particular, 7.3, 8.4.2, 10.5.2, and 10.5.4.)

There seem to be two basic types of paper in the journals, depending on whether new data is offered or a new theory. The first is the data type of paper, which may also be called the experimental or factual type. An example is the famous Michelson-Morley paper which, in 1887, reported the absence of a measurable ether drift influencing the speed of light.

The second type of paper is the theoretical type which works out the analytical effects of some new physical or mathematical concept. An example is Einstein's first paper on relativity (1905), which explained conceptually the null result of the Michelson-Morley experiment. Of course, some papers are a combination of the first two types, as will be seen.

12.2.2   Experimental Papers

The experimental paper presents the results of some significant new experiment, and, as far as the author wishes to go, argues to a conclusion based on these results. The argument may be either inductive or deductive, but it must employ the new data (which is equivalent to a particular, or minor, premise in a logical sequence).

OUTLINE FOR EXPERIMENTAL PAPER

Abstract
Introduction (includes purpose, scope, previous work in field)
Experimental Procedure
Experimental Data Analysis
Conclusions
Acknowledgments

Comparison with actual experimental investigation outlines in the journals shows that this outline can be shortened for many applications. In one paper in *The Physical Review*, for instance, *Experimental Data Analysis* and *Conclusions* were combined in a single heading: *Results and Discussion*.

In a longer paper offering a more complicated argument, the experimental work suggested a generalization of theory, and this generalization was made and confirmed. The paper thus presented a combination of experimental and theoretical results. The outline headings included *Abstract, Introduction, Experimental Procedure, Generalization of Formula, Results,* and *References*.

12.2.3   Theoretical Papers

The theoretical paper introduces some new theory or concept and works out the logical consequences. The new concept may be mathematical or physical, or it may apply to equipment design or to an operating procedure. Whatever sort of idea it is, it must lead to a prediction, or perhaps to an equipment design, which can be tested and verified by experiment.

Abstract
Introduction
Theoretical Analysis
Applications
Conclusions
Appendix

This outline includes a full deductive sequence (see 8.4.2.1). An outline for reporting the investigation of a new concept in equipment design is usually also a deductive sequence. It might include *Abstract, Introduction, Design and Construction, Tests of Technique, Recommendations.*

12.2.4 Additional Information on Organization

Most scientific journals are flexible in their approach to outlining, one of the chief considerations being the saving of space. The author of a prospective paper is advised in all cases to study the journal itself for information. The editorial masthead of the cover (front or back) may contain important information. The journals of the AIAA (American Institute of Aeronautics and Astronautics)—that is, the *AIAA Journal, Journal of Aircraft,* and *Journal of Spacecraft and Rockets*—carry on their back covers excellent instructions entitled "Information for Contributors to Journals of the AIAA."

The American Institute of Physics *Style Manual* (which can be purchased from The American Institute of Physics for a nominal fee) has valuable information on all aspects of preparing a scientific paper. It discusses, for instance, the essential characteristics of the Summary, Conclusions, and Recommendations. The Summary is most likely to conclude a paper which presents data and explanation, rather than an argument. It should only summarize material that has already been presented, and it should keep the same relative emphasis.

Conclusions are convictions which have resulted from consideration of the material presented. They must stem directly from the material presented, and they should be foreshadowed in the Introduction, where the purpose of the paper appears. However,

Conclusions do not generally appear in full at the beginning, as in technical reports.

Recommendations do not appear in those papers where new knowledge alone is developed. Recommendations involve a course of future action based on the new information, and are more appropriate in technical reports than in scientific papers. Some papers have a special section on Nomenclature appearing before the Introduction. This section lists and defines all special symbols used in the paper.

12.3   THE THESIS

The thesis is a long research paper written by a college student, ordinarily in fulfillment of one requirement for a degree. A thesis manual issued by the college may give explicit instructions on preparation to the student, and the discussion here must complement the information appearing in such a manual.

A thesis, which is ordinarily prepared and written over a college term or year, includes at least four stages of preparation. These stages are (1) selecting a topic in consultation with a faculty advisor, (2) performing research on the topic, (3) organizing the research material, and (4) writing the thesis.

12.3.1   Selecting Thesis Topic

When selecting a thesis topic, the student and his advisor must consider many points. The project should require some genuine research, including a library literature search. The topic selected should be interesting to the student, and should be approached, furthermore, with an open mind. In other words, the logical outcome of the research should depend solely on the research itself. Limitations of college research facilities should be considered, including laboratory space, materials, and apparatus, as well as adequacy of library documentation. The cost involved and time required are also important. The latest trends in science are a useful consideration in selecting a topic, for research experience gained in a thesis investigation can be an advantage later in job placement.

The faculty thesis advisor can give excellent advice, but the advisor should not be treated as a research assistant or literary consultant. Information which can be found in the library should not be asked of him.

12.3.2   Thesis Research

Thesis research which is to be performed in the library can be studied in Chapter 13. Research areas open to consideration (besides the library and laboratory) include interviews with experts, field trips, and questionnaires.

When all research has been accomplished, the student should possess documented information of the following nature: (1) laboratory data and plots, (2) mathematical analysis where appropriate, (3) library research notes and cards, (4) results of questionnaires, (5) interview notes, and (6) field trip observations. (Of course, not all these sources are appropriate for all theses.) The next task is to reduce this raw data into a coherent form for the thesis.

12.3.3   Organization of Thesis Material

The thesis outline which follows contains numbered headings. These are often appropriate for a thesis, which generally is much longer than a scientific paper.

OUTLINE FOR THESIS

Abstract

    I. Introduction (discusses importance of subject, scope of subject, gives brief summary of research problem, approach, and conclusions)

    II. Literature Survey (discusses important documents relating to subject, traces historical growth of subject, may refer to References or Bibliography)

    III. Problem Analysis (states new concept or new experimental approach, develops this in subsections such as Experimental Equipment, Data Analysis, Comparison with Theory)

    IV. Discussion of Results (summarizes results, explains negative results, discusses strengths and weaknesses of technique, suggests future work)

    V. References (or Bibliography)

Special thesis sections which may be required include *Nomenclature, Acknowledgments,* and *Appendixes.*

12.3.4   Rewriting Thesis as Scientific Paper

The problem of rewriting a thesis as a scientific paper for submission to a journal often comes up. Solution of this sometimes awkward problem may require strategical planning. How can a comprehensive, perhaps eighty-page document be cut, pasted, rewritten, and stapled to best serve as a typing draft for a highly compressed eight-page paper? If the problem proves insoluble—and it sometimes does—then the best course is to begin anew from a fresh standpoint.

A general comparison of the two documents in question will be useful. The thesis usually has a lengthy introduction and literature survey, which should be radically pruned in a scientific paper. Indeed, the *Style Manual* of the American Institute of Physics suggests that the introduction and literature survey be restricted to one or two paragraphs. The student can take it for granted that much information which was new to him is already well known to the specialists of the scientific community. Under these circumstances, it may be best to write a new introduction and literature survey.

The problem analysis of the thesis (or body of the report) usually includes a discussion of the experimental setup and a data presentation and analysis. These sections are appropriate for a scientific paper, but, of course, require great compression. It is particularly important in rewriting the problem analysis to eliminate subordinate detail and ruthlessly compress statement of the main points. Any redundant data presentation (in both tables and curves, for instance) should be eliminated.

The question of pruning mathematical analysis is always difficult. The "This deduction is obvious" technique can be used more freely in a scientific paper, but here too it has limits which the analyst must judge for himself.

Something must be said here in praise of rewriting, drab as the task may seem. It is only in rewriting that conscious, disciplined writing skills can be cultivated by the novice. This results because, in rewriting, the concern is perhaps wholly with organization, sentence structure, and the formal requirements of good style. At first these requirements were subsidiary to supplying meaning itself. But in writing the second or third draft, the student can become so annoyed at his foolish mistakes that he never makes them again.

12.4   MANUSCRIPT PRESENTATION AND PROOF

12.4.1   Work Sheet for Contributors to Journals

This textbook recommends that the student, engineer, or scientist use either a required style guide in the preparation of a manuscript or the *Style Manual* of the American Institute of Physics. (See 11.1.4 for a discussion of style guides.) Some of the conclusions of the *Style Manual* appear in a work sheet (Section VII of the manual), which is reproduced here.

WORK SHEET FOR CONTRIBUTORS TO JOURNALS

1. *Preview.* An author should study the form and style of printed articles in the journal to which he proposes to contribute. Editors of scientific journals vary in their attitudes toward departures from traditional forms of spelling and style, as well as in the burdens of responsibility that they impose upon themselves for what may be termed the literary quality of their journals. In spite of their best efforts, authors can scarcely prevent occasional stylistic divergences in what they write from the recommendations of this manual. An editor corrects occasional slips gladly and without much expenditure of time. But if an author consistently violates recommendations, whether intentionally or not, it is almost certain that the editor, for lack of time, will have to return the manuscript with a request that it be altered to conform with accepted practice. To be on safe ground, therefore, and to give the editor what help he can in maintaining consistency in the journal, an author must perforce adhere quite closely to recommendations.

2. *Manuscripts.* Manuscripts must be in English, typewritten, double spaced, on one side of the paper, on $8\frac{1}{2}$- by 11-inch durable, opaque, white paper. The typed original, not a carbon or other duplicated copy, should be submitted. Wide margins at the top and bottom and sides must be provided to permit editorial instructions to the printer. Editorial work will be speeded if a duplicate, including copies of illustrations, is submitted in addition to the original. An author should adopt a particular way of writing his name in the by-line and use this same name for all his publications. This practice makes indexes more useful and less confusing.

3. *Figures.* Line drawings should be planned for reproduction to the 3-inch column width. The portion to be reproduced should be, preferably, 5½ or 8¼ inches wide and should not be larger than 8½ by 11 inches. Lettering and symbols should be large enough so that they will be at least 1/16 inch high after reduction. Lines should be broad and black, since a narrow line will appear as a broken, gray line after reduction.

The original line drawings must be submitted. They must be in India ink on white or pale blue tracing paper or tracing cloth. Coordinate paper should not be used unless lines are light blue and main lines are drawn in India ink.

Photographs of apparatus should be used sparingly, since a good line drawing tells more than most photographs. Oscillograph photographs should be avoided in most cases by making a line drawing from the photograph. Pictures should be glossy prints with a maximum black and white contrast and should be rectangular in shape. Do not write heavily on the backs of pictures or clip or staple them so as to mar the picture.

Plan figures to use space efficiently. Avoid wasting space, particularly at the top or bottom.

Write on the back or margin of each illustration the figure number, the author's name, and the name of the journal. Figures should be numbered consecutively. Figure captions should be typed, double-spaced, and included as the last page of the manuscript. Captions are sent to the printer, but figures are sent to the photoengraver. Every figure should have a caption.

Refer to figures in the text by the abbreviation "Fig. 1," etc., except at the beginning of a sentence where "Figure" is not abbreviated.

4. *Mathematics.* As much of the mathematical material as possible should be typewritten; any handwritten material should be carefully printed. Be sure to distinguish between capital and small letters. Indicate clearly superscripts by a black penciled $\vee$ sign under the superscripts and subscripts by a penciled $\wedge$ sign over the subscript. Avoid complicated subscripts and superscripts, subscripts to subscripts, and superscripts to superscripts. Avoid repetition of a complicated expression by use of an appropriate symbol for the expression. Identify Greek letters by underlining in red, and identify unusual symbols by number. Use fractional exponents instead of root signs. Use the solidus (/) for simple fractions to save vertical space. Remember that the typesetter is neither a physicist nor a mathematician.

Refer to equations in the text as Eq. (1), etc., except at the beginning of a sentence where "Equation" is not abbreviated.

5. *Footnotes.* Footnotes in the text should be numbered in a

single sequence in order of appearance and arranged thus:

[1]A. B. Smith, Phys. Rev. **41**, 852 (1932).
[2]H. Lamb, *Hydrodynamics* (Cambridge University Press, Cambridge, England, 1940), 6th ed., pp. 573, 645.

6. *Tables.* All but the simplest tabular material should be organized into separate tables. Tables should be numbered with Roman numerals and typed on sheets at the end of the running text. Each table must have a caption, typed at the top of the table, which makes the data in the table intelligible without reference to the text. Complicated column headings should be avoided. If necessary, use symbols which are explained in table footnotes.

7. *Abstract.* An abstract must accompany each article. It should be adequate as an index and as a summary. It should give all subjects, major and minor, concerning which new information is presented. It should give the conclusions of the article and all numerical results of general interest. An abstract is usually reprinted verbatim in abstract journals. Therefore, great care should be used in writing it.

8. *Correspondence and alterations.* Editors appreciate the responsibility some laboratories take for the excellence of manuscripts sent out, but they prefer to correspond directly with the author rather than through executives or through the reports division of the author's laboratory. Please do not send to the editor any correspondence about proof, reprints, or publication charges.

If a paper is accepted for publication, an author is so notified by the editor of the journal. Alterations can be made at the time of acceptance. Any subsequent alteration is costly. After a paper has been accepted, correspondence about proof, reprints, and publication charges should be sent to the Publication Manager, American Institute of Physics, 335 East 45 Street, New York 17, New York.

9. *Proof of articles.* Proof will be sent to the author and should be returned promptly to the Publication Manager. A few alterations in proof are unavoidable, but the cost of making extensive alterations or of correcting mistakes caused by careless preparation of the manuscript will be charged to the author.

10. *Check list.*

(a) Double-space typed original manuscript.
(b) Original line drawings of figures, not larger than 8½ x 11 inches.
(c) Abstract.
(d) Typed list of figure captions.
(e) Mathematical expressions explained for the printer.

(f) Greek letters underlined in red and unusual symbols identified in the margin.

(g) Additional copy of manuscript and figures, if available.*

12.4.2   Concluding Remarks

The many requirements for the preparation of a technical paper
make a severe chore for the potential author. Indeed, he probably
finds it impossible to perform with the zest of Sir Isaac Newton,
reported in 12.1.1. The modern writer has resources, however,
which Newton did not. These are mainly the resources of his
supporting institution, possibly including a typist, a draftsman, or
an entire publications group. Furthermore, the publication fees
which Newton often paid the printer (or which friends paid to
prod Newton on) are now usually paid by the supporting institution. Finally, as a result of strong, modern editorial discipline, the
writer does not now have to suffer all the painful contention and
improper criticism which, it appears, finally drove Newton into
theology.

*Reprinted by permission of the American Institute of Physics.

13 *Library Research and Reference*

RESEARCH AND REFERENCE FUNCTIONS

The function of a modern technical library is to bring the scientist or engineer who wishes specialized information into contact with that set of technical documents which can best provide him this information. The scientist or engineer must first provide some clue, or set of clues, which can help the library begin the search for these documents. These clues may include title, author, date of publication, issuing agency, report number, call number, and classification number. Most often, however, the clue is a fuzzy subject-clue—"I want some information on thermodynamics," or "Can you tell me the best reference book on Laplace transform theory applied to dashpots?"

With the best bag of clues he can obtain, the researcher (or research librarian) enters a document catalog and begins a search, whose nature will be explained more fully later. During the search he proceeds from, perhaps, "dashpots" to document call number and abstract. If the abstract satisfies him, he proceeds next (by the call number location coding) to the particular place in the files where copies of the document are stored.

There are two aspects to organizing a technical research library. One aspect is obtaining and storing the necessary documents themselves, in anticipation of their need. The other aspect is organizing a cross-coded file connecting call number, document, description, and location in such a manner that entry into the file with any kind of clue can lead to the desired document with reasonable dispatch.

13.1.1   Nature of Research Problems

Technical research libraries can be set up to provide information at three levels of application. These levels can be categorized roughly as (1) scientific, (2) engineering, and (3) popular. Most technical libraries provide some documentation at all three levels. Each tends, in the main, however, to serve either engineering most broadly or science most broadly. Scientific research, of course, occurs at the forefront of basic knowledge and is increasingly mathematical in nature. The basic problem of engineering research is usually a determination of the state of the art; that is, a determination of the most advanced types of useful equipment it is practicable to build, considering cost and period of service.

The popular literature of most technical libraries consists of science and engineering news magazines and magazines which offer broad informal reviews of the work being accomplished in selected fields. These reviews and state-of-the-art surveys are usually written for the scientist or engineer who is new to the field.

13.1.2   Nature of Documentation

Technical library documents can be divided into three overlapping classes; namely, (1) books, (2) periodicals, and (3) reports. Books include textbooks, bound reference works, bound abstracts, catalogs, directories, yearbooks, bound treatises of all sorts, and bound collections. The periodicals include magazines, newspapers, newsletters, scientific and engineering journals, and abstracting journals.

The reports classification is probably the most confused of all, but it is also the area in which the most striking advances have been made recently in library technology. This class of documents includes technical reports written by universities and research and development institutions, both for their own purposes and for such government agencies as NASA, Department of Defense, Atomic Energy Commission, Department of Commerce, and Department of Agriculture. These agencies, of course, conduct important research and development programs of their own and issue large numbers of reports, too. Many of these are of the scope and importance of books and, even though paperbound, are classified as books by some librarians. Other librarians undoubtedly classify such documents as reports, tending to add confusion to an already bewildering situation.

13.1.3   Traditional Card Catalogs

In order to learn what the recent advances of library technology (or information retrieval) are, we must first review the traditional document classification schemes. The information contained in this subsection should be understood as applying to almost all the libraries, including public libraries, existing at the time of World War II.

Documents in the traditional public library are usually all listed and described in the card catalog, with at least one card per document. The periodicals, for instance, are listed on these cards in alphabetical order according to their titles. The nonfiction books are listed alphabetically on three or more separate cards; one card lists by author or source agency, another by title, and a third by principal subject. (Reports are usually not carried as such by the traditional library, and will not be discussed at this point.) All these cards are organized in a strict alphabetical sequence in the card catalog, whatever their nature, and each card (except for additional cross-referenced subject cards) usually carries a full citation, or description, of the document.

The order of the cards in the card catalog is not the order of the documents on the shelves, of course. Still, the card catalog must model the book stacks in such a manner that information on the card will indicate shelf position. This is the central problem which all library cataloging schemes must solve. How does position in the catalog, or fingerprint file, relate to position in the shelves? This question is easily solved for periodicals. Usually there is a periodical room or section in which newspapers hang on racks in the alphabetical order of their titles and in which magazines appear in two separate alphabetical sequences, the first sequence representing current issues and the second representing bound issues of back volumes.

Nonfiction books, however, are not organized on the shelves according to their titles. They are ordered according to their subject classification number. (Works of fiction are ordered, of course, according to the alphabetical sequence of their authors' last names.) Subject classification schemes represent an important organizing concept and must be given careful scrutiny. Such schemes make the implicit assumption that all subjects (nonfiction) about which books will possibly be written can be placed in correspondence with a numerical sequence (or letter-number sequence). In other words, all subjects can be graded like students in a classroom. Such a grading scheme must indicate all subjects and must assign them all different numbers.

13.1.4   Traditional Subject Classification

The two familiar systems of subject classification are the Dewey Decimal and the Library of Congress systems. The classification number each of these schemes assigns to a document determines the sequential order in which the book appears in the book stacks. The call number of a document (found on the left upper corner of the card) is the subject classification number plus the book number (which codes special information about the book, such as publisher, author's initials, and number of copies on file in-house).

13.1.4.1   DEWEY DECIMAL CLASSIFICATION

The Dewey Decimal system for subject classification places all possible subjects within ten broad categories of knowledge. These categories and their assigned number ranges are as follows:

CALL NUMBER RANGE	SUBJECT CATEGORY
000–100	General Works
100–200	Philosophy
200–300	Religion
300–400	Social Sciences
400–500	Language
500–600	Pure Science
600–700	Technology
700–800	The Arts
800–900	Literature
900–1000	History

All engineering knowledge appears within the number range 600–700 in the "Technology" category of the Dewey Decimal classification. To accommodate the multitude of new engineering topics generated in the last few decades, it has been necessary to develop a finer and finer decimal substructure within the assigned range. For instance, in one library, the book *Jane's All the World's Aircraft* (McGraw-Hill) has been assigned the classification number 629.133. This fine decimal substructuring of engineering knowledge may remind the physicist of the finer substructuring of the electromagnetic spectrum created by such phenomena as the Zeeman and Stark effects.

13.1.4.2 LIBRARY OF CONGRESS CLASSIFICATION

The Library of Congress classification system was created to answer criticism of the Dewey Decimal classification. One criticism was that insufficient number space was accorded the more rapidly developing fields of knowledge, such as engineering and social studies. The Library of Congress system, furthermore, provided a method of assigning uniform call letters for all libraries for any given document (a book's subject matter generally being open to different classifications when a standard classification is not provided).

The Library of Congress system is now used in many of the nation's new libraries. It assigns all knowledge to twenty-four broad categories, each category being denoted by an initial capital letter. A partial list of these follows:

P. Language and Literature
Q. Science
R. Medicine
S. Agriculture
T. Technology
U. Military Science
V. Naval Science

All engineering books are cataloged with the initial letter T, and all science books with the initial letter Q. A second letter, followed by numbers, further subclassifies the subject of the work. (Some documents are classified in each system by more than one subject. The secondary subjects are usually placed on cross-referenced subject cards.) In the Library of Congress system, QA denotes mathematics; QB, astronomy; QC, physics; and QD, chemistry. Going further, QA101 denotes arithmetic and QA538 denotes analytic geometry. The letters and numbers which often appear on the second and third lines of a call number in either system, as already noted, provide coded data about the book, such as publisher, author's initials, and number of copies on file.

The student who wishes further information about subject classification can consult his librarian or obtain a bulletin of the appropriate classification association. A continual updating of these classification systems must occur to accommodate new areas of knowledge, and the classification association provides this service.

13.1.5   Reference Books

The traditional technical library has a reference room or reference section in which are grouped all standard reference books. These books consist of dictionaries, encyclopedias, atlases, gazetteers, yearbooks, bibliographies, biographical reference books, statistical collections, buying guides, and newspaper and magazine indexes and abstracts.

A mixed and abbreviated list of standard reference works which the student should already know (or take the trouble to look up) includes *Webster's Third New International Dictionary, Encyclopedia Britannica, Roget's International Thesaurus, Facts on File, The Aerospace Year Book, Books in Print, American Men of Science, The New York Times Index, Statistical Abstract of the United States, Thomas Register, Readers' Guide to Periodical Literature, Introduction to the History of Science, Who's Who in Engineering, The Columbia Lippincott Gazetteer of the World,* and *The American Oxford Atlas.*

There are many newer, more specialized reference works dealing with science and technology which can be listed, such as the following:

1. *Electronics and Nucleonics Dictionary,* by Nelson Cooke and John Markus (McGraw-Hill).
2. *Encyclopedic Dictionary of Electronics and Nuclear Engineering,* by Robert Sarbacher (Prentice-Hall).
3. *The International Dictionary of Applied Mathematics* (Van Nostrand).

4. *IRE Dictionary of Electronic Terms and Symbols*, Institute of Electrical and Electronics Engineers.
5. *Chambers Technical Dictionary*, edited by C. F. Tweney and L. E. C. Hughes (Macmillan).
6. *Dictionary of Guided Missiles and Space Flight*, edited by Grayson Merrill (Van Nostrand).
7. *McGraw-Hill Encyclopedia of Science and Technology*.
8. *The Harper Encyclopedia of Science*, edited by James R. Newman (Harper & Row).

13.1.6   Abstract Services

Another important class of reference documents is the science and engineering journal indexes and abstracts. A modern technical library will carry several of these, including the *Physical Abstracts, Chemical Abstracts, Nuclear Science Abstracts, Electrical Engineering Abstracts, Solid State Abstracts, International Aerospace Abstracts, The Engineering Index, Computer Abstracts,* and *Applied Science and Technology Index.* (Report abstracts will be discussed later.) These volumes, usually accumulated at least once each year, present short abstracts of all papers appearing in their field of interest in the scientific journals for that year. (Some of the indexing volumes merely cite the articles and papers, rather than present full abstracts.) During the current year (before the annual volume can appear) the abstracts for each volume appear in various monthly or quarterly paperbound installments. These installments are collected at the year's end to make up the annual volume.

The scientist or engineer who wishes to follow research progress in his specialty monitors his subject classification in the proper abstracting journal, and thus discovers quickly what new directions have been taken. The monthly installments may provide only subject indexes, but the annual volumes provide more elaborate cross-indexes, such as author and source.

13.1.7   Technical Library Problems

The information explosion beginning with World War II has been said to have more than tripled the technical information available to man. This astonishing and heartening proof of the efficiency of modern research has furnished increased problems as

220

well as payrolls to technical libraries across the nation. The peculiar problems of modern information retrieval are not necessarily solved by spending more money, however; some of the new problems are the following:

1. The logarithmic growth in number of new books and reports, literally threatening to turn into paper swamps those libraries whose facilities have not increased logarithmically also.
2. The librarian's difficulty in evaluating and cataloging new information because of its increasing, narrow specialization. Adding to this problem are the important works which must be translated from such languages as Russian.
3. The inaccessibility of many important documents because of military security requirements and proprietary information requirements.
4. The financial inability of many technical journals to publish the large backlog of papers they have already accepted. Many worthy papers become lost because they must be published in some obscure house organ, or are only accessible to friends of the author.
5. After discovery, the decreasing time span during which new information must become available if it is to be useful. The difficulty is that unless new work is published almost at once, it may be repeated somewhere else, with consequent loss of time and research funds; or perhaps the building of expensive new equipment will be based on inadequate information.
6. The difficulties experienced with language itself in the processes of subject classification, abstracting, coding, and indexing. Traditional subject classification schemes are too complicated and "unmechanical." They should be simplified and clarified to provide a less ambiguous, more convenient passage from subject to call number. In addition, they should be set up to reduce the amount of file space required, if possible.

13.2 INFORMATION RETRIEVAL THEORY AND APPLICATION

13.2.1 Information Retrieval Functions

13.2.1.1 INTRODUCTION

Any discussion of technical library problems assumes that high-speed digital computers and electronic data-processing systems can be applied to aid in the solution. Computers, without doubt, have enormous capabilities for memorizing, cross-indexing, and routine classifying and filing. They are used even now to perform many traditional library functions. For instance, the card catalog is replaced in some technical libraries by a computer memory. The computer receives new document entries via punched card. It may also receive circulation information. From this data it can print out, on demand, new library accession lists each week or month, corrected catalog lists each month, book overdue lists, title lists, abstracts within a selected subject category, and even mailing lists of patrons.

On the other hand, the computer cannot of itself evaluate new documents for purchase, perform document classification without supervision, or write abstracts. These operations require the evaluation of ideas rather than numbers, and the computer, of course, has not yet ventured into this dubious realm.

In the paragraphs which follow, a librarian's work will be organized in a series of sequential steps, and the application of new techniques to these steps will be examined.

13.2.1.2 DOCUMENT SELECTING AND ABSTRACTING

The choice of documents for a technical library must be made by the librarian or perhaps by a supervisory committee appointed to aid him. In addition, most technical libraries order documents in answer to requests from patrons, provided the budget can accommodate these requests. Often, responsible agencies such as NASA and the Department of Defense offer a broad selection of free reports, and these, too, are received and stored. In the long run, however, some useless and even incorrect documents are received, and other documents go out of date quickly, filling the files with a heavy, fading burden of information, like shopworn goods.

A national document-evaluation service of some kind would probably aid harried librarians greatly in keeping up to date. It could grade all new documents in terms of worth, and perhaps downgrade these documents from time to time until they can finally be dropped. Such a service would require great, broad skill in grading, but, even if crudely accomplished at first, could be useful.

Document selection usually cannot be performed by anyone without a good abstract at hand to judge from. Many technical documents carry their own abstracts, and others can be found abstracted and evaluated in review journals. Still, the librarian himself, in the long run, must weigh the claims of one document against another document from perhaps a totally different field, making the best attempt he can at abstracting and evaluating. It would be convenient if computers could help him in this practice, but of course they cannot write abstracts. They can, however, perform a curtailed form of abstracting called *descriptor indexing*, described next.

13.2.1.3   INDEXING AND CATALOGING

The indexing of documents is a central function of any library. Indexing indicates whether a given document is available, and if so, where to find it. The catalog is the register of this information for all documents. Subject classification indexing has already been described. The newer methods can be described as *coordinate-concept indexing* or (used in a more restricted sense) *descriptor indexing*.

Descriptor indexing is the assigning of a set of coordinate, or equally important, words and expressions to characterize a document uniquely by all its concepts. The descriptors are somewhat similar to subject headings, but not so broad. When the descriptors are not assigned, but actually picked out of the title, headings, or text, they are often called *keyterms*, or *uniterms* (this selection can be accomplished by a computer programmed with such data as the title, headings, and abstract).

The document is usually also assigned a code number, which is its "name" to the computer. The code number is not related in any forced way to the descriptors. In fact, it is often the same as the accession number (which merely gives the year and relative order in which the document was received by the library).

An example of a descriptor set which might be used to index a report on "reentry" is *ablation, nose cone, boundary layer, Ajax II, Phase II program,* and *upper atmosphere.* Given a set of six or eight similar descriptors for each document, a computer can easily make up a complete catalog of all accessions. This is accomplished by listing all descriptors alphabetically and by citing each document under any descriptor assigned to it. The document described by the six sample descriptors would be entered in six different locations. When the computer prints out the com-

Library Research and Reference   223

plete catalog (usually in a volume somewhat like a telephone book), the researcher can enter the catalog under *ablation, nose cone, Ajax II,* etc., and discover the wanted document, as well as others. However, very few documents will be listed under all six descriptors, and thus the search for titles is very quickly narrowed.

13.2.1.4 SEARCHING AND CODING

It is very cheering to observe that a computer can search through its own descriptor catalog in the same way that a man can search through a printed-out catalog. Given any set of descriptors, the computer can quickly print out a list of those documents whose descriptors perfectly match the set it was given. Thus, the computer can perform an effective literature search, using descriptors.

A little more must be stated about coding. The title, author, source agency, descriptors, shelf location, circulation information, and number of copies can all be filed in memory in terms of the code number; conversely, once this number is known, all other information can be obtained. The printed-out catalog will usually have cross-indexes in terms of author, source agency, title, etc., to aid the researcher who begins with limited information. Each cross-index gives at least the code number, and the code number index gives complete information about the document, including abstract.

13.2.1.5 STORING DOCUMENTS

The extent to which a computer should actually store the text of technical documents in its own memory is debatable. Of course, it must store descriptors and citation information to aid in literature search. It might even store abstracts and print these out on demand. But, sad to say, any more elaborate mechanization of a library would require more elaborate financing than libraries ordinarily can provide. Probably for the early future, most technical libraries will continue to store their documents in traditional ways, including storage on microfilm in addition to shelf and file storage of the documents themselves.

The researcher who requires microfilmed documentation can either obtain the film from the librarian and view it on the illuminated screen of a microfilm reader or request that it be printed out for his permanent possession by some process such as Xerox.

The various report services to which many technical libraries subscribe (to be discussed in 13.3) often furnish only microfilm reports to member libraries, so microfilm facilities are a requisite in these cases.

Another method for avoiding the costly purchase and storing of many bulky technical documents is furnished by certain library associations. These associations may pool their documentation in a general or union catalog and make this available to the patrons of all the member libraries. In most cases, requests for interlibrary service are filled by photocopying the wanted material. When more than perhaps twenty pages are required, the book itself may be sent out to the patron, subject to certain restrictions.

13.2.1.6 PRESENTATION AND DISSEMINATION

Research can be made available in a library by giving possession of the document, by giving possession of a photocopy of a limited number of pages, or by giving possession of microfilms of wanted pages for photo viewing.

In specialized applications of a computer, whole procedures or parts lists are carried in memory and updated there as convenient, then are printed out on demand. These techniques, however, are considered to be report processing techniques rather than library services.

Many technical libraries offer document translation service upon request. There are also many specialized services which can be offered to individual research groups, such as specialized group files and indexes. These services may include the use of auxiliary indexing, searching, and readout devices, in addition to the card catalog and computer-printed catalog. Some of the auxiliary indexing and searching devices include punched cards, edge-notched cards, optical-coincidence (peekaboo) cards, magnetically coded plastic cards, and magnetic tapes.

Dissemination of library information includes printing and distributing accession lists, special request notices, circulation notices, and documents. Most of these functions can be, and are, efficiently computerized. Dissemination of accession lists should be especially prompt because of the fact that technical documents are subject to rapid outdating and because equipment being built may require design changes as a result of new information. Generally, one accession list goes to all patrons, but where specialized research groups are functioning, it may be useful to direct special information on new documents to special groups.

13.3   SPECIAL REPORT CATALOGS

The subject of report catalogs and bulletins is separately discussed here because of the relative newness and importance of this topic. Indeed, report cataloging can be considered one of the most important results of information retrieval work since World War II. No longer must the research described in technical reports throughout the nation suffer the sort of fate described by John Keats when, near his deathbed, he penned his own epitaph: "Here lies one whose name was writ in water." The Keats name, of course, has been rescued from obscurity, and so have the names of the authors of many technical reports. Such technical rescue work was probably first accomplished by the former Armed Services Technical Information Agency (ASTIA). The function of this agency, now known as the Defense Documentation Center of the Defense Supply Agency (DDC), will be discussed here, as well as the function of the NASA *Scientific and Technical Aerospace Reports* (*STAR*) service. The Atomic Energy Commission, the Department of Commerce Office of Technical Services, and other public and private groups also have report cataloging services.

13.3.1   *DDC Technical Abstract Bulletin (TAB)*

The DDC *Technical Abstract Bulletin* (*TAB*) is an important instrument for all who propose to work on defense research and development programs. This bulletin is issued semimonthly without charge to all qualified organizations who do business in the field of government-sponsored research. It prints abstracts of all reports received by the agency from its numerous contractors and certain others during the time period the bulletin covers. The semimonthly issue (in magazine form) gives report abstracts listed in thirty-three distinct subjects of military and technological knowledge. These subjects range from (1) Aircraft and Flight Equip-

226

ment and (2) Astronomy, Geophysics, and Geography to (33) Transportation.

There are two distinct but similar sections to each *TAB*. One section, printed on white paper, lists reports open to unlimited circulation; the other section, printed on buff paper, cites reports of limited circulation which presumably are vital to national defense.

Within each subject, the technical reports are cited and abstracts given in the order of their accession. This accession order is coded for each document by its *AD* number, or "accessioned document" number, as *AD-948 167*. Usually the number of reports listed in a subject category for a given half month is small enough to be quickly scanned by the researcher, and elaborate cross-indexing is not needed. However, the semimonthly bulletins are accumulated at longer intervals in indexes which provide descriptor and source headings.

The researcher brings to the *TAB* accumulated index several descriptive words or phrases associated with his technical problem, and these descriptors he looks up in the alphabetical listing. Under each one he may find several appropriate titles and report *AD* numbers.

The researcher who wishes to obtain a report he has discovered must fill out a short request form and give it to his own librarian. If the library does not already have the report, the request goes to one of the regional offices of DDC. A photocopy is usually supplied promptly to organizations holding government research contracts.

13.3.2 **NASA *Scientific and Technical Aerospace Reports* (STAR)**

The NASA *STAR* catalog is, like the *TAB* bulletin, a semimonthly abstract service (also gathered in accumulated indexes over longer time intervals). It is available free to government agencies and contractors, and goes out on a subscription basis to libraries in general. (Restricted NASA reports are available in a separate catalog of limited circulation, called *CSTAR*.)

The *STAR* documents all relate to the science and technology of aerospace, and may include reports not funded by NASA. The *STAR* listings include all documents which have not been published in journals or in monograph or book form. (The latter class of documents is listed separately in a companion catalog, the

International Aerospace Abstracts bulletin, published at alternate intervals with *STAR*. The *International Aerospace Abstracts* bulletin is published by The American Institute of Aeronautics and Astronautics, or AIAA.) The two companion aerospace bulletins thus abstract and catalog all known aerospace literature of merit (including significant foreign accessions). This private and governmental teamwork constitutes a unique and valuable publishing service to scientists and engineers of the nation.

The *STAR* bulletin resembles the *TAB* bulletin in usage, with more indexes and with some differences in the method of classifying technical reports and accumulating indexes. The researcher who wishes to obtain a *STAR* report fills out a request form which he submits to his librarian. He receives his document, in return, usually in the form of a microfilm copy.

The *STAR* bulletins are organized on the basis of thirty-four subjects, or categories, of all aerospace knowledge. These subjects have become the basis for report catalogs prepared by many corporate aerospace libraries, and will be reproduced here as information of genuine importance to the technical writer. The numbers associated with each subject are not to be thought of as subject classification numbers, because they do not break down into a decimal substructure. They are merely coded headings under which the computer organizes each separate catalog of reports. (The *TAB* headings, likewise, do not break down into a decimal substructure.)

01	Aerodynamics
02	Aircraft
03	Auxiliary Systems
04	Biosciences
05	Biotechnology
06	Chemistry
07	Communications
08	Computers
09	Electronic Equipment
10	Electronics
11	Facilities; Research and Support
12	Fluid Mechanics
13	Geophysics
14	Instrumentation and Photography
15	Machine Elements and Processes
16	Masers
17	Materials, Metallic

18 Materials, Nonmetallic
19 Mathematics
20 Meteorology
21 Navigation
22 Nuclear Engineering
23 Physics, General
24 Physics, Atomic, Molecular, and Nuclear
25 Physics, Plasma
26 Physics, Solid-State
27 Propellants
28 Propulsion Systems
29 Space Radiation
30 Space Sciences
31 Space Vehicles
32 Structural Mechanics
33 Thermodynamics and Combustion
34 General

Grammatical Terminology

Active. A type of verb inflection. See V*oice*.

Adjective. A part of speech used to modify a noun or pronoun. The following are types of adjectives:

1. DESCRIPTIVE: A *faulty* tube, a *red* resistor
2. LIMITING: A missile, *an* airplane, *the* rocket
3. NUMERICAL: a. Cardinal: *one* diode, *four* relays
        b. Ordinal: his *first* lesson, the *ninth* wave
4. PRONOMINAL: a. Demonstrative: *this* orbit, *that* launch, *those* errors
        b. Indefinite: *any* system, *each* employee, *no* cause
        c. Interrogative: W*hose* pencil? W*hich* triangle?
        d. Possessive: *my* turn, *your* move, *his* name
        e. Relative: *whose, which, what* (not as questions)

Adverb. A part of speech used to modify a verb, adjective, or another adverb. The following are examples of each type of modification:

1. VERB: He designed bombs *cleverly.*
2. ADJECTIVE: He was *well* known.
3. ADVERB: He worked *very* carefully.

231

Agreement. The requirement that the subject and verb of a sentence, or a pronoun (or pronominal adjective) and its antecedent, agree in number, person, and possibly gender. For example, the third-person singular form of the subject requires the third-person singular form of the verb.

Antecedent. The substantive to which a pronoun or pronominal adjective refers. The antecedent may be either a noun, phrase, or clause.

Appositive. A substantive (usually a phrase) used in a parenthetical restatement of another substantive. Example: Take the procedure—*the one I wrote*—to the data office.

Article. A limiting form of adjective. *The* is called the definite article; *a* and *an* are called indefinite articles.

Attributive Noun. A noun used as an adjective. Example: The *amplitude* ratio is small.

Auxiliary. A helping verb form, such as *did, ought, may,* and *might.* The auxiliary verbs help form the voices, modes, and tenses of the principal verbs.

Cardinal Number. An ordinary number, such as *one, eight, ten.*

Case. The manner in which a noun or pronoun is positioned or inflected for use in a particular sentence. There are three case forms of inflection in English: nominative, possessive, and objective. Nouns do not change to show the nominative and objective cases, but usually add *'s* (singular), or *s'* (plural) to show the possessive case. The personal pronouns change to show use in all cases, as follows:
1. NOMINATIVE. The case used as the subject of a verb or as a predicate noun: *I, you, he, she, it, we, they.*
2. OBJECTIVE. The case used as the object of a verb, verbal, or preposition: *me, you, him, her, it, us, them.*
3. POSSESSIVE. The case used to show ownership or origin: *my, your, his, her, its, our, their.*

Clause. A naturally occurring group of words having a subject and predicate. There are two types, the independent (or principal) and the dependent (or subordinate) clause.

232

1. INDEPENDENT. Clause which makes an independent statement. A simple sentence is an independent clause; every sentence contains at least one such clause.
2. DEPENDENT. Clause which does not make a complete or independent statement. It is usually introduced by a subordinating conjunction, and acts in the sense of either an adjective, adverb, or noun.

    Adjective: The information *which you gave me* was wrong.

    Adverb: I gave it to you *before it was checked*.

    Noun: The short circuit proved *that the design was faulty*.

Collective. A noun which implies a collection of things in its singular form (*group, class, majority*).

Colloquial. The language of familiar conversation or of informal letters.

Comparison. Inflection of an adjective or adverb. There are three degrees of comparison: positive, comparative, and superlative.
1. POSITIVE. The normal form of an adjective or adverb: *good, cold, quickly*.
2. COMPARATIVE. Form of an adjective or adverb which indicates comparatively increasing (or decreasing) degree of modification: *better, colder, more quickly* (or *less quickly*).
3. SUPERLATIVE. Form of an adjective or adverb indicating the greatest or least degree of modification: *best, coldest, most quickly* (or *least quickly*).

Examination of the examples will show that there are three different ways in which adjectives and adverbs can be inflected. For short adjectives and some adverbs (such as *soon*), the usual change is to add the suffix *er* for the comparative degree and *est* for the superlative degree. For longer adjectives and for most adverbs, these degrees are indicated by combination with *more* (or *less*) and *most* (or *least*). Some adjectives (*good*) and adverbs (*well*) have a completely irregular comparison. Some adverbs (*here, now, then*) have no comparison at all.

Complement. A word or phrase following a verb which completes the sense of the statement made by the verb. There are four types of complement: direct objects and indirect objects following transitive verbs and predicate nouns and predicate adjectives following linking verbs.

1. DIRECT OBJECT: I carried my *lunch* to work.
2. INDIRECT OBJECT: I gave the *plunger* a push.
3. PREDICATE NOUN: The Gemini is a *spacecraft*.
4. PREDICATE ADJECTIVE: The damage was *widespread*.

Complex. Describes a sentence containing one independent clause and at least one dependent clause.

Compound. Describes a sentence containing two or more independent clauses. Also describes any word or phrase compounded by the use of a coordinating conjunction; examples are *time and tide*, and *quickly and efficiently*.

Compound–Complex. Describes a sentence which contains two or more independent clauses and at least one dependent clause.

Conjugation. The modifications or changes in a verb form which show all possible uses of the verb in a sentence. A verb may change to show person, number, tense, voice, and mode. A simple conjugation of the verb *tell* is presented, restricted to the indicative mode, present tense. The possible changes in person, number, and voice are shown.

	ACTIVE VOICE		PASSIVE VOICE	
	Singular	*Plural*	*Singular*	*Plural*
1st person:	I tell	We tell	I am told	We are told
2nd person:	You tell	You tell	You are told	You are told
3rd person:	He (she, it) tells	They tell	He (she, it) is told	They are told

There is also a type of conjugation of the verb relating to the three possible forms of statement: simple (*I go*), progressive (*I am going*), and emphatic (*I do go*).

Conjunction. Word used to link other words, phrases, or clauses. There are two types: coordinating and subordinating.

1. *Coordinating.* Connects like sentence elements only.
   a. Simple: *and, or, but, for, yet, nor*
   b. Correlative: *either . . . or, neither . . . nor, both . . . and, not only . . . but also*
2. *Subordinating.* Connects dependent with independent clauses.
   a. Simple: *although, until, since, if, as, that, when*
   b. Correlative: *although . . . yet, if . . . then, since . . . therefore*

Conjunctive Adverb. An introductory or transitional adverb used not to modify the verb but to show the logical relation between independent clauses. Examples are *however, moreover, thus, hence, therefore, then,* and *consequently.*

Connective. A conjunction, a preposition, or sometimes a relative pronoun.

Coordinate. Elements of a sentence that are paired or doubled by a coordinating conjunction.

Copula. A linking verb. See *Linking.*

Dangling Modifier. A modifying word or phrase which, through some fault of sentence construction, lacks a substantive or verb to modify. Dangling modifiers are usually participle and infinitive phrases which have no substantive to modify. Example: *Having followed directions,* the cake tasted delicious.

Declension. A type of inflection. See *Inflection* and *Case.*

Demonstrative. See *Adjective* and *Pronoun.*

Diction. Word choice, particularly as regards accuracy of meaning.

Ellipsis. The intentional omission of a word or words from a sentence. The omitted words are usually necessary to make the grammatical structure of the sentence complete but may not be necessary to transmit its meaning. An example of such a sentence is *If convenient, stop and see him.*

Finite Verb. Verb form which is capable of being used as the predicate of a sentence. These forms, such as *go, could have been, will be seen, had attempted,* are contrasted with the nonfinite forms, or verbals. The verbals include the gerunds, participles, and infinitives.

Gender. The property of certain nouns and pronouns which implies the sex of the object represented. There are four genders in English:
1. MASCULINE: *boy, bachelor, rooster, James, he, uncle*
2. FEMININE: *girl, heroine, Jane, her, hers, aunt*
3. NEUTER: *sky, pencil, truth, steel, it*
4. COMMON: *child, them, anyone*

Grammatical Terminology   235

Gerund. A verb form which is used as a noun and ends in *ing*. In addition to acting as a noun, the gerund may take an object or may be modified by an adverb, thus forming a gerund phrase. Examples of gerunds are *hunting, traveling,* and *flying.*

Idiomatic. Adjective describing expressions which, though illogical or impossible to translate word for word into a foreign language, are accepted as correct usage. *Guard against its happening* and *put up with* are examples of idiomatic expressions.

Indicative. See *Mode.*

Infinitive. The normal form of the verb (*run, jump*) preceded by the word *to,* as *to run, to jump.* The infinitive is an extraordinarily flexible construction, acting in particular cases either as a noun, adjective, or adverb. In all these forms it retains many of the properties of the original verb.

1. INFINITIVE AS NOUN. As a verbal construction, the infinitive can have the properties of a substantive (*To read* is my hobby). It may be used either as a subject, object, or predicate noun. In all these varied uses, the infinitive can have the present tense (*to strike*) or the perfect tense (*to have struck*). It can also have either the active voice (*to strike*) or the passive voice (*to be struck*). The infinitive can have a subject, or a complement, or be modified by an adverb.
2. INFINITIVE AS MODIFIER. The infinitive may serve as an adjective (I bought a compass *to guide me*). It can also serve as an adverb (He wanted *to go*).

Inflection. Those changes in the form of a word which show how the word is used in a particular sentence. There are three types of inflection: conjugation, declension, and comparison.

1. CONJUGATION. Changes in the verb form which show person, number, tense, voice, and mode.
2. DECLENSION. Changes in the form of a noun or pronoun which show case, person, number, and gender.
3. COMPARISON. Changes in the form of an adjective or adverb which show relative degree of application. The three degrees are *positive, comparative,* and *superlative.*

Intensive. Compound personal pronoun used for emphasis (He came *himself*).

Interrogative. Asks a question. Said of a sentence, adverb, pronoun.

236

Intransitive. See *Verb*.

Inverted. Describes a group of words in which some part of the normal word order is reversed. A sentence may be inverted for the sake of variety in expression, as *Out of nowhere came the hero of the West*.

Irregular. Describes a verb which forms its many tenses by internal changes rather than by adding suffixes: *get, got, gotten*. This type of verb is sometimes called a strong verb.

Jargon. Unnecessarily difficult or complex technical phraseology. This term can be applied to technical language which is poorly adapted to the technical level of the reader.

Linking. Describes a verb which implies existence or appearance, rather than asserting an action. Examples are *is, seems*, and *appears*. This type of verb is followed by a predicate noun or predicate adjective rather than by an object.

Masculine. See *Gender*.

Mode. Type of verb inflection. There are three possible modes of a verb: indicative, imperative, and subjunctive.
1. INDICATIVE. Asserts a fact or condition or asks a question.
2. IMPERATIVE. Expresses a direct command or a request: *Carry on! Turn the selector switch off. Please remain in your seats.*
3. SUBJUNCTIVE. Expresses a concession or condition which is untrue or doubtful. This mode is indicated by the use of a plural verb with a singular subject, as *I wish I were going with you*. The subjunctive mode is a literary form of statement little used in technical writing.

Modify. To limit or define more strictly the meaning of a word in a particular application. Substantives are modified by adjectives (or groups of words used as adjectives). Verbs are modified by adverbs (or groups of words used as adverbs). Adjectives are modified by adverbs, and adverbs are modified by other adverbs.

Motion Verb. Transitive or intransitive verb.

Nonrestrictive. Said of a modifying word or group of words. A nonrestrictive modifier does not define, narrow, or restrict the meaning of the word modified; rather, it adds extraneous information not necessary to the correctness or independence of the statement.   Example: Clark Street, *which runs parallel to Lakewood,* is the best route to travel.

Noun.   A part of speech which names a person, place, object, or idea.   There are five types of noun: common, proper, collective, concrete, abstract.   Some of these types overlap.

  1. COMMON NOUN.   Name common to all members of a class of things: *boy, dog, city, man, tool.*
  2. PROPER NOUN.   Name given to a particular member of a class (always capitalized): *Los Angeles, John Kennedy, Apollo, Ford.*
  3. COLLECTIVE NOUN.   Name identifying a group or collection: *equipment, majority, herd, regiment, stuff.*
  4. CONCRETE NOUN.   Name of a physical or material thing perceptible to the senses: *tree, book, smell, smile.*
  5. ABSTRACT NOUN.   Name of a quality or concept: *truth, love, average, trajectory.*

Number.   The inflectional characteristic of a noun, pronoun, pronominal adjective, or verb which indicates that either one thing (singular) or more than one thing (plural) is under consideration.

  1. SINGULAR: *it, he, mine, apple, is, adds, Clara.*
  2. PLURAL: *they, you, are, nieces, Johnsons.*

Object.   A substantive which completes the assertion made by a transitive verb.   There are two types of object: direct and indirect.

  1. DIRECT OBJECT.   Object which receives the primary action asserted by the verb, as in "A missile struck the *target.*"
  2. INDIRECT OBJECT.   Object indirectly or secondarily affected by the transitive verb, as in "He would give *you* the shirt off your back."   The indirect object can usually be associated with an omitted preposition, such as *to* or *for.*

Objective.   See *Case.*

Objective Complement.   A noun or adjective that completes the sense of a direct object, as in "He called the statement a *mistake.*"

Ordinal Number.   Adjective indicating place, rank, or order of succession, as *first, tenth, eighty-ninth.*

Parallel Structure.   The use of an identical grammatical structure to record each of a succession of ideas which are logically parallel. This principle can be applied to the objects named in a simple series by making each member, for instance, a plural noun (*zin-*

238

nias, asters, and *roses*), or by making each member a modified plural noun (*orange zinnias, yellow asters,* and *red roses*). A more complex series of actions might be described in repeated prepositional phrases, as in "He went *to the bank, to the hardware store, to the post office,* and then *to work.*" The Bible gains much simplicity and majesty of statement from its use of parallel phrasing. Key clauses from the Lord's prayer, for instance, all have a parallel imperative form: ". . . hallowed be thy name," ". . . give us this day," ". . . forgive us our trespasses," ". . . lead us not into temptation," ". . . deliver us from evil. . . ."

Parenthetic Element. A word or group of words wedged into a statement independently of the statement's grammatical structure. Parenthetic elements are usually strongly punctuated by commas, dashes, or parentheses to show the break in grammatical structure. Example: Hypergolic fuels—*it was explained to me*—ignite readily on contact.

Participle. A verb form used grammatically as an adjective. Unlike an adjective, however, the participle may take an object. It also has both active and passive forms. There are two types of participle: present and past.

1. PRESENT PARTICIPLE. The present participle always ends in *ing,* as *laughing* and *designing.* In the following sentence, the present participle *having* takes the object *time: Having no time,* I did not attend the cryogenics lecture.

2. PAST PARTICIPLE. The past participle generally ends in *ed,* but it may end in *n* or *t* or be formed irregularly by an interior change of the verb; examples of each type are *hunted, fallen, burst,* and *brought.* In the following sentence, the passive form of the past participle *encouraged* is used: *Having been encouraged* by our success, we continued the research.

Particle. Word which has no inflectional changes and no referent. The prepositions, conjunctions, and some adverbs are particles.

Parts of Speech. A general classification of words according to their usage in a sentence. There are eight formal parts of speech: noun, pronoun, adjective, verb, adverb, preposition, conjunction, and interjection.

Passive. A type of verb inflection. See *Voice.*

Person. Inflection of verbs, personal pronouns, and pronominal adjectives to indicate the part played in an assertion by any of three possible persons: the speaker (first person), the person addressed (second person), or the person, idea, or thing spoken of (third person). Each person may be indicated in either the singular or plural sense. Inflections of the personal pronouns and the verb are shown in the following simplified present-indicative conjugation of the verb *to be* (active voice).

	SINGULAR	PLURAL
First person:	I am	We are
Second person:	You are	You are
Third person:	He (she, it) is	They are

Phrase. A small, naturally occurring group of words without a subject or predicate. The formally defined phrases are the prepositional, appositive, and verbal phrases. These are all used as single parts of speech in a sentence. Informal phrases include the verb and its auxiliaries and such phrasal conjunctions and prepositions as *on condition that, in order that, as soon as, according to,* and *about the size of.*

Plural. See *Number.*

Possessive. See *Case.*

Predicate. A word or group of words, usually following the subject of a sentence or of a clause, which asserts some action or condition with regard to the subject. The complete predicate includes the complete verb and any modifiers and complements (. . . *has tuned the oscillator carefully*). The simple predicate includes the principal verb and any auxiliary verbs (. . . *has tuned*).

Predicate Adjective, or Noun. See *Complement.*

Preposition. A part of speech used to introduce a modifying phrase, called a prepositional phrase. Examples are *to, on, of, by, toward,* and such compounds as *on account of, according to,* and *in connection with.* Many prepositions can serve equally well as adverbs (*after, down, through,* and *beyond*).

Principal Parts. The three forms of the verb from which all verb inflections can be derived. These forms are the present infinitive, the first person singular of the past indicative, and the past participle. The principal parts of the regular verb *look* are *look, looked, looked,* and of the irregular verb *speak* are *speak, spoke, spoken.* The first principal part of the verb forms the present tense; it also forms the future tense when compounded with the auxiliary verbs *will* or *shall.* The second principal part forms the past tense. The third principal part (when compounded with the auxiliary verb *have*) forms all the compound (perfect) tenses of the active voice. The passive voice is formed throughout with the third principal part, compounded in all forms with *be.* In all perfect tenses the passive is also compounded with *have.* In the future tenses it adds *will* or *shall.*

Pronoun. A part of speech used as a substitute for a noun. There are five types of pronoun: personal (including compound personal), relative (including compound relative), interrogative, demonstrative, and indefinite. (Some of these types may overlap.)

1. PERSONAL. Inflected pronoun showing by its form whether reference is made to the speaker, to the person addressed, or to another person (or object or idea). Examples are *I, me, you, her, his, their,* and *it.* The compound personal pronouns include such forms as *ourselves, myself, yourself, himself.* Compound personal pronouns are used for emphasis; for example, "He came *himself.*" They can also indicate a reflexive action, as in "He hit *himself.*"

2. RELATIVE. The simple relative pronouns are *who (whose), which, that,* and *what.* Combinations such as *whoever, whosoever, whichever,* and *whatsoever* are called compound relative pronouns. The relative pronouns not only replace nouns but also serve as connectives introducing subordinate clauses; for example, "The salesman *who* came will demonstrate the computer."

3. INTERROGATIVE. A pronoun used to introduce a direct or indirect question. There are three such pronouns: *who, which,* and *what.* An example of such usage is "*Which* shall I say you prefer?"

4. DEMONSTRATIVE. The demonstrative pronouns are *this* and *that* (including the plural forms *these* and *those*). These pronouns should not be confused in usage with the demonstrative adjectives. An example of correct pronoun usage is "*That* is my best subject."

5. INDEFINITE. Pronouns which do not refer to definite persons

or things. Some of the common indefinite pronouns are *any*, *another*, *someone*, *each*, *several*, *both*, and *everything*.

Redundancy. Needless repetition of words and meaning. Example: Return that voltmeter *back* to the stockroom.

Reference. The relation between a pronoun or pronominal adjective and the noun for which it stands or to which it refers. The two words should agree in person, number, and gender.

Referent. The object, person, quality, etc., which a word represents.

Regular. Said of a verb which forms its principal parts in a regular manner (*discuss, discussed, discussed*).

Relative. See *Pronoun*.

Restrictive Modifier. A modifying element which defines or restricts the word it modifies rather than adding casual or extraneous information about the word. Example: The house *on the left* is mine.

Sentence. A group of words containing a subject and predicate which makes a complete and independent assertion. Every sentence contains at least one independent clause. There are four types of sentence: simple, compound, complex, and compound-complex.
1. SIMPLE. Sentence which contains one independent clause. An independent clause may be in the indicative, imperative, or subjunctive mode. It may either make a declarative or interrogative statement. This statement may be in the active voice or it may be in the passive voice.
2. COMPOUND. Sentence which contains two or more independent clauses.
3. COMPLEX. Sentence which contains one independent clause and at least one dependent clause.
4. COMPOUND-COMPLEX. Sentence which contains two or more independent clauses and at least one dependent clause.

Singular. See *Number*.

Split Infinitive. An infinitive form in which some modifier follows *to* and precedes the verb, thus separating the two parts of the infinitive (*to quickly deduce, to satisfactorily have been able*).

242

Subject. A word or group of words, usually placed at the beginning of a sentence or clause, which names the person, place, object, or idea about which an assertion is made. The simple subject is always a substantive and the complete subject is this substantive together with its modifiers. Examples of complete subjects are *The reason I called . . .*, *The rational numbers between nine and forty-seven . . .*, *The airplane wing. . . .*

Subjunctive. See *Mode.*

Subordinate. Modifying, or introducing a modifying element.

Substantive. A word or group of words which names a person, place, object, or idea. Nouns, pronouns, gerunds, noun clauses, and verbal phrases used as nouns are all substantives.

Syntax. The rules for organization of words in phrases, clauses, and sentences.

Tense. That form of verb inflection which indicates the time at which the action or condition named by the verb occurs. There are three simple tenses: present, past, and future. There are three compound or perfect tenses: present perfect, past perfect, and future perfect. Similar tenses exist for other modes and voices of the verb.

Term. A word used in one sense only. Certain words have two or more distinct meanings (*fly*, for instance, used as a noun or verb). When only one of these meanings is intended, the word is properly described as a *term.*

Transitive. See *Verb.*

Verb. A part of speech used to express an action, condition, or state of existence. There are several types of verb, including transitive, intransitive, linking, and auxiliary.
    1. TRANSITIVE. Expresses an action which is carried through the verb and directed to some complement. The active transitive verb takes a direct object, as in "The cow gives *milk.*" Sometimes, in addition, it takes an indirect object, as in "The cow gives the *farmer* milk." In this case, a preposition such as *for* or *to* can usually be inserted before the indirect object.

Grammatical Terminology   243

2. INTRANSITIVE. Expresses an action performed by the subject which is complete in itself, needing no complement; for example, "The boat *rocked*."
3. LINKING. See *Linking*.
4. MOTION. Transitive or intransitive verb.
5. AUXILIARY. See *Auxiliary*.

Verbal. Form of the verb which may be used as another part of speech. See *Gerund, Infinitive, Participle*.

Vernacular. Denotes the informal and social part of the language, as opposed to the formal and technical part.

Voice. A form of inflection applied to verbs. Voice denotes the part played by the subject with regard to any action asserted by the verb. There are two voices, active and passive.
1. ACTIVE. In this voice, the action of the verb is directed toward an object: "He *dropped* an atom bomb." The subject performs the action.
2. PASSIVE. In this voice, the subject of the sentence receives the effect of the action: "The atom bomb *was dropped*."

B Structure of Word Groups

The binary diagrams, or trees, for word groups discussed in Chapter 3 are presented here. These trees are described as *binary* because each element is paired. This sort of pairing makes for most efficient coding in a digital network. At the human level, it can furnish a convenient structural index for the intricacies of grammar and syntax.

WORD CLASSIFICATION TREE

A word classification tree is presented first. Two new groups of words have been named: "basic" words and "auxiliary" words. The former include substantives and verbs. Elementary sentences can be written with basic words alone; for example, *Bandits rob bank*. The auxiliary words serve the purpose of modification and variation of the basic structure, as in *Several mean and ugly bandits robbed the city bank last night at ten o'clock*.

It will be noted that the verbs have been separated at the parts-of-speech level into their two basic forms, linking verbs and motion verbs. The linking verbs picture a static, eternal universe; the motion verbs picture a dynamic, changing universe in which time and change in time are explicitly recorded by the sentence form. Because the sentence forms which these verbs generate are so fundamentally different, it seems reasonable to classify them as different parts of speech.

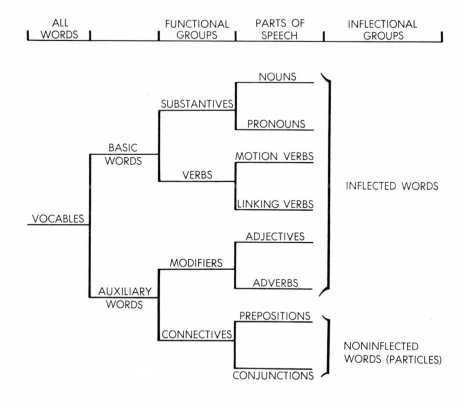

NOUNS

PRONOUNS

SUBSTANTIVES

MOTION VERBS

LINKING VERBS

VERBS

BASIC WORDS

INFLECTED WORDS

VOCABLES

ADJECTIVES

ADVERBS

MODIFIERS

AUXILIARY WORDS

PREPOSITIONS

CONNECTIVES

NONINFLECTED WORDS (PARTICLES)

CONJUNCTIONS

I. Word classification tree

PHRASE AND CLAUSE CLASSIFICATION TREE

All formal types of phrase and clause are presented on this tree, organized in a binary structure. It might be complained that appositive phrases do not appear. This is true for the reason that an appositive phrase is not an independent part of sentence structure. It serves the exact structural purpose of the word for which it stands, or which it restates. Thus, the appositive phrase usually serves the function of a substantive word. This classification tree is not so neatly grouped as the first one. There are many empty slots where, possibly, other phrase and clause forms could have been inserted had they been needed in speech. But obviously they are not needed and so can be dismissed from any description of usage.

SENTENCE CLASSIFICATION TREE

All basic sentence forms of the indicative mode are classified on this tree, with classification being based on the verb form. The verb is so fundamental to sentence structure that the substantives need not be considered. The compound, compound-complex, etc., type of sentence classification is not basic, for it deals only with the manner in which clauses can be combined. The form of the clause itself is being considered here.

It is easy to dismiss these structural trees as being restatements of what has already been stated many times in the past. But the trees offer more than description. They offer a solution to the question, for instance, "Is a passive sentence a transitive sentence?" The structural tree answers this question in the affirmative.

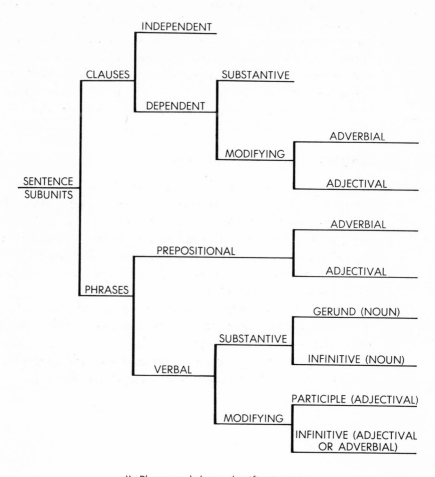

II. Phrase and clause classification tree

248

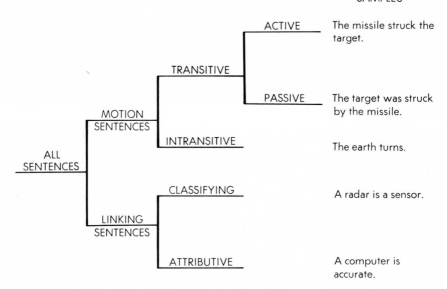

SAMPLES

ACTIVE — The missile struck the target.

TRANSITIVE

PASSIVE — The target was struck by the missile.

MOTION SENTENCES

INTRANSITIVE — The earth turns.

ALL SENTENCES

CLASSIFYING — A radar is a sensor.

LINKING SENTENCES

ATTRIBUTIVE — A computer is accurate.

III. Sentence classification tree (indicative mode)

Structure of Word Groups 249

Index

Abbreviations, 139
Abstract catalogs, 220, 226–229
Abstracting, 222–223
Abstracts, 212
  in reports, 138
Accession numbers, 223
Active voice, 55, 244
Addison, Joseph, 10
Adjectives, 231, 246
  comparison of, 233
  order of, 71, 94–95
Adverbs, 231, 246
  comparison of, 233
  limiting, 94
  order of, 71, 94–95
Aerodynamics, 6, 16–17
Agreement, 52–54, 98, 232
AIAA, 206, 228
Ambiguous reference, 100–101
American Institute of Physics *Style
  Manual*, 187, 206, 209, 210–213
*American Standards for Drawings,
  Symbols and Abbreviations*, 187
Amerine, M. A., 133–134
Ammonia vapor reproduction, 190–191
Analog words, 97

Analogy, 113–114
Analysis, verbal, 103–104
Antecedents, 52, 98, 232
Appendixes, 138–139
Appositives, 232
Archimedes, 6
Architecture, 7–8
Argumentative writing, 107–114, 203
Aristotle, 6, 9, 108
Articles, 90, 232
Artificial order, 134–135
Astrolabe, 8–9
Attitude stabilization, 127–130
Attributive nouns, 232
Audience, 20, 24–26
Auxiliaries, conditional, 64–65
Auxiliary verbs, 64–65, 232
Aviation Week & Space Technology, 52

Bacon, Francis, 9, 21–22, 113
Bacon, Roger, 8
Bible, 120–121, 135, 239
Bibliographies, 139
Binary nature of grammar, 48, 245
Black, Susan, 47

251

Block diagrams, 127–130
Body of report, 118
Bragg, William, 115–116
Brevity, 28–29
Burglary, 47

Caesar, Julius, 7, 122
Card catalogs, 216–217
Cardinal numbers, 232
Case, 97–98, 232
Cataloging, 216–217, 223–224
Caution in writing, 64–65, 203
Chalk, 11–12
Chaucer, Geoffrey, 8–9, 80
Check list for manuscripts, 212–213
Clarity, 28–29, 70
Classification, 45–46, 91–92
Clauses, 49, 232–233, 247–248
  order of, 70–72, 94
  symmetry of, 68–69
Coding, document, 39–40, 223–224
Collective nouns, 99–100, 233
Colloquial language, 233
Communication, symbolic, 35, 43
Communications satellites, 17–18
Comparison, grammatical, 96–97, 233
Complements, 70–72, 77, 233–234
Complex sentences, 234, 242
Complexity, measures of, 67–68
Compound sentences, 234, 242
Compound-complex sentences, 234, 242
Compression in writing, 202–203
Computers, use of, 37–40, 174, 178, 221–222
Conclusions section, 206–207
Conditional statements, 64–65
Configuration control plans, 170
Confusing sentences, 88–97
Conjugation, 234
Conjunctions, 74–75, 234, 246
Conjunctive adverbs, 72–73, 235
Connectives, 49, 235, 246
Consumer Reports, 122
Contents section, 137
Coordinate elements, 74, 235

Coordinate indexing, 223
Copulas, 235
Countdown procedures, 125–126, 177–178
Covers, 136
Critical spirit, 4
CSTAR report abstracts, 227
Cult words, 86–87
Curtiss, Glenn, 16

Dangling modifiers, 59–60, 92–93, 235
  infinitive type of, 93
  participle type of, 92–93
Darwin, Charles, 11, 111
Darwin, Francis, 111
data, datum, use of, 99–100
Data reports, 173–174
DDC Technical Abstract Bulletin, 226–227
Decimal headings, 139–140
Declensions, 235
Deduction, 104–105, 108–111
  Aristotelian, 9
  errors in, 109–111
  as outline sequence, 123–124
Definition, 45–48, 133
Descartes, 109
Descriptive writing, 114–116
Descriptors, 40, 223–224
Development proposals, 164–165
Dewey Decimal system, 217–218
Diazo dye, 190
Diction, 90–91, 235
Digital words, 97
Dissemination of documents, 225–226
Distaste for writing, 31, 201–202
Distribution lists, 139, 196–197
Ditto reproduction, 191
Document selection, 222–223
Documentation, 162–163, 215–216
Dryden, John, 10

Editing, 144, 192–195
Editor, technical, 181–185

252

Egyptian writing, 2
Einstein, Albert, 204–205
Electron, discovery of, 115–116
Electronic data processing, 39, 178
Electrostatic reproduction, 189–190
Ellipsis, 89–90, 96, 235
Emphasis, 78–82
Enthusiasm, 32
Errors, of number, 98–100
   of reference, 100–101
Experimental investigation reports,
   172–173
Experimental papers, 205
Expository reports, 144–149
Extended definition, 46–47

Facilities plans, 168
Fallacies, verbal, 110–111
Falstaff, 123–124
Faulty classification, 91–92
Faulty comparison, 96–97
Faulty word choice, 90–91
Federal prose, 30
Feedback, 129
Figures, 211
Filters, verbal, 20–21
Finite verbs, 235
Flow diagrams, 127–130
Fog Index, 67–68
Footnotes, 173, 211–212
Forewords, 137
Framework sections, 135–136
Franklin, Benjamin, 13

Galen, 8
Galileo, 6, 8
Garbling, 193
Gender, 235
Generalizations, 113–114
Gerunds, 236
Gibbs, Willard, 15–16
Glossaries, 139
Gobbledygook, 30
GPO Style Manual, 185–186

Grammar, 231–244
   compared with style, 143–144
Grammatical coupling, 203

Haldane, J. B. S., 105–107
Handbooks, 131–132, 178
Heading systems, 139–140
Hemingway, Ernest, 22–24, 29–30
Henry, Joseph, 14–15
Herodotus, 4
Holmes, O. W., 15
Holmes, O. W., Jr., 48
Homer, 3–4
Huxley, T. H., 11, 55, 104–105, 127

I, use of, 56–57
Idiomatic expressions, 236
Iliad, 3
Illustrations, 137, 211–212
Illustrations group, 188–189
Imperative mode, 55, 62, 237
Impersonal usage, 58, 201–202
Indefinite pronouns, 99, 241–242
Index, Fog, 67–68
Indexing, document, 39–40, 223–224
Indicative mode, 62, 237
Inductance, 14–15
Induction, 104–105, 111–114
   Baconian, 9
   errors in, 113–114
   as outline sequence, 124–125
   statistical, 114
Induction-deduction, 123–124,
   172–173, 205
Infinitives, 95, 236
Inflection, 49, 236, 246
   errors in, 97–100
Information retrieval, 221–229
Information theory, 36
Intensives, 236
International Aerospace Abstracts, 228
Interrogatives, 236
Intransitive verbs (see Verbs)
Introductions, 118, 208

Inverted constructions, 67, 237
Investigation reports, 172–175
Irregular verbs, 237
It, use of, 52–55

Jargon, 237
Johnson, Samuel, 10–11, 30–31, 46
Journals, scientific, 204, 206, 210

Keyterms, 223
Kompfner, R., 56–57

Langley, S. P., 16
Language sources, 40–42
Legal review, 197–198
Libraries, 214–217
    associations of, 225
    problems of, 220–221
Library of Congress system, 218–219
Lightning, 13–14
Limiting adverbs, 94
Lincoln, Abraham, 68–69, 79
Linguistics, 42–43
Linking verbs, 49, 237, 245–246
Lists, 75, 137
Literature searching, 224
Logical signposts, 72–73
Logistics support plans, 170
Lucretius, 8

Mailing the report, 199
Maintenance plans, 169–170
Management proposals, 165–166
Manhattan Project, 18
Manuals, 81, 131–132, 178–180
Manufacturing plans, 168
Manuscripts, 210–213
Master copy, 189–191
Matches, book, paper, 144–149
Mathematics, 34–35, 211
Mather, Cotton, 12–13
Matrices, 48

Medieval science, 8
Memory in communication, 35
Memory level, 69–70
Mendeleef, 122
Michelson-Morley experiment, 204–205
Microfilming documents, 224–225
Mnemonic aids, 126
Mode, 55, 62, 237
Modification, 237
    order of, 71–72
    as subordination, 77–78
Modifiers, dangling, 92–93
Motion or flow, order of, 126–131
Motion verbs, 49, 237, 245–246
Motivation in writing, 20–21, 31–32, 201
Multilith, 192

Narrative writing, 114–116, 155–157
NASA, 163, 187, 226–229
New words, 144
New Yorker, The, 10, 30
Newton, Isaac, 9, 112, 201, 213
Nomenclature, 139, 207
Non sequitur, 110
Nonfiction, types of 102–103
Nonrestrictive modifiers, 237–238
Normal sentence order, 70–72
Nouns, 49, 238, 246
Novum Organum, 9
Number, 238
    errors of, 98–100
Numeral-letter headings, 140

Objective complements, 238
Objects, 238
Offset printing, 191–192
One, use of, 57
Ordinal numbers, 238
Organization of material, 26–28, 204–207
Orwell, George, 84
Outlining sequences, 119–120, 135–136

Outlining sequences, artificial order in, 134–135
  deductive order in, 123–124
  defining order in, 133–134
  formal logical order in, 123
  inductive order in, 124–125
  motion or flow order in, 126–131
  operational order in, 131–132
  random order in, 134–135
  relative magnitude order in, 134–135
  time order in, 125–126
Ozalid, 190–191

Paper book matches, 144–149
Paragraph unity, 80–82
Parallel structure, 74–76, 238–239
Parenthetic elements, 239
Participles, 59–60, 92–93, 239
Particles, 239, 246
Parts of speech, 49, 239, 246
Passive voice, 58–60, 239
Patent notices, 138, 198
Peloponnesian War, 4–5
Personal pronouns, 60–61, 240
Phonetic writing, 43–44
Photocopying documents, 225
Photographs, 188, 211
Photo-offset printing, 191–192
Phrases, 240, 248
  order of, 70–72, 94
  writing with, 83–84
Pierce, J. R., 17–18, 56–57
Plataea, siege of, 4–5
Pliny, 8
Plural, 238
Pope, Alexander, 3
Popular science, 11–12
Population trends, 158–161
Position, importance of, 79
Possessive case, 232
Predicate adjectives, 70–72, 233–234, 237
Predicate nouns, 70–72, 233–234, 237
Predicates, 240
Prefaces, 137

Prepositions, 95–96, 240, 246
Principal parts, 240–241
Printing, 191–192, 198
Procedures, 39, 126, 177–178
Program summary plans, 167–168
Progress reports, 176–177
Pronouns, 241–242, 246
  errors in use of, 100–101
  recommended uses of, 60–61
Proof sheets, 212
Proposals, 163
  cult words in, 86–87
  development types of, 164–165
  management types of, 165–166
  specimens of, 149–155
  study types of, 163–164
Proprietary information, 138, 198
Prose style, 10
Proto-German, 42–43
Publications department, 181–185

Quality assurance plans, 170
Quality control reports, 175

Radar, 27, 179–180
Random order, 134–135
Recommendations section, 207
Redundancy, 84–85, 242
Reference, 242
  ambiguity in, 100–101
  loss of, 202
Reference books, 219–220
References section, 139
Referents, 44, 242
Regular verbs, 242
Relative pronouns, 241
Relative magnitude, order of, 121–123
Relativity, 204–205
Reliability, 170–171
  plans for, 170–171
  reports on, 176
Repetition, 80–82, 84
Reports, 162–163
  abstract catalogs for, 226–229

Reports, editing of, 192–193
    processing of, 195–199
    review of, 193–194, 197–198
    sections of, 136–139
    specimens of, 142
        analytical types of, 158–161
        expository types of, 144–149
        narrative types of, 155–157
        proposal types of, 149–154
Reproduction processes, 189–192
Reproduction typists, 187–188
Restrictive modifiers, 242
Reviewing reports, 193–194, 197–198
Rewriting, 209–210
Royal Society, 10–11, 13
Russell, Bertrand, 37

Satellites, 17–19
Saturn booster, 122–123
Science writing, 9, 61
Scientific American, 17, 30, 133
Scientific and Technical Aerospace
    Reports (STAR), 227–229
Scientific papers, 204–205
Scope, statement of, 118–119
Searching, literature, 224
Security classification, 198
Semantics, 47–48
Sentences, 242
    classes of, 49, 247, 249
    confusing types of, 88–97
    excessive length of, 202–203
    faulty classification in, 91–92
    indexes for, 67–68
    normal length of, 67
    normal order of, 70–72
    symmetry of, 68–69
    variety in, 66–67
Sequences, outlining (see Outlining
    sequences)
Series construction, 75–76, 97
Singular number, 238
Sizzi, Francesco, 113
Specifications, 171–172
Spirit reproduction, 191

Split infinitives, 95, 242
Spock, Dr. Benjamin, 24–28, 57
Sprat, Thomas, 10
STAR report abstracts, 227–229
Statistical induction, 114
Storing documents, 224–225
Study proposals, 163–164
Study reports, 174–175
Style, 28–31
    emphasis by, 80
    grammar compared with, 143–144
    problems of, 194–195
Style guides, 185–187, 210
Subject, knowledge of, 20–24
Subject classification, 217
Subjects, 243
Subjunctive mode, 55, 237
Submarine control, 149–154
Subordinate constructions, 77–78, 243
Substantives, 243, 245–246
Summaries, 138, 206
Suppressed premises, 109–110
Syllogisms, 108–109, 123–124
Symbolic logic, 36–37
Symbolic writing, 43
Symbols in text, 139, 188, 211
Symmetry in sentences, 68–69
Syntax, 42, 243
Synthesis, 103–107

Tables, use of, 137, 212
Technical Abstract Bulletin (TAB),
    226–227
Technical editor, 181–184
Technical reports group, 183–185
Ten Commandments, 135
Tenses, 243
    recommended use of, 62–65
Terminology, 45, 154–155
Terms, 45, 243
Test plans, 168–169
Test reports, 172
Theoretical papers, 205–206
Thermodynamics, 15
Theses, 207–210

Thucydides, 4–6
Time sequence, order of, 125–126
Title pages, 137
Tolstoy, Leo, 30
Training plans, 170
Transitive verbs (*see* Verbs)
Translation, 37–39
Trees, classifying, 49–50
  for phrases and clauses, 247–248
  for sentences, 247, 249
  for words, 245–246
Trip reports, 155–157
Tristram Shandy, 73–74
Trivial statements, 87–88
Typing group, 187–188

Uniterms, 223
U.S. Government Printing Office
  Style Manual, 185–186

Variety in writing, 28–29, 66
Varitypists, 188
Verbal fallacies, 110–111
Verbals, 244
Verbs, 243–244, 245–246
  order of, 70–72
  origin of, 41
  recommended tenses of, 62–65
  types of, 49

Vernacular, 244
Vitruvius, 7
Voice, 58–60, 244
Vulcan, 3

We, use of, 56–57
Weak words, 85–86
Whatmough, Joshua, 2
Whitehead, A. N., 112–113
Wine, 133–134
Word count, 67
Words, 45–50
  choice of, 90–91
  classifying tree for, 245–246
  coining of, 143–144
Wordy sentences, 83–88
Work sheet, 210–213
Writing, nonfictional, 102–103
  argumentative type of, 107–114
  descriptive type of, 114–116
  expository type of, 103–107
  narrative type of, 114–116
  with phrases, 83–84

Xerox, 189–190, 225

You, use of, 55–56